Eugenia Parry

CRIME ALBUM STORIES

Paris
1886–1902

Scalo

Zurich – Berlin – New York

Eugenia Parry has written numerous books and essays on art and early photography, notably: *The Art of French Calotype* with André Jammes (1983); "L'Art d'un collectioneur: Henri LeSecq Photographe," in *Henri LeSecq Photographe 1850–1860* (1986); *The Photography of Gustave LeGray* (1987); *Louis DeClercq* (1989); "Edgar Degas's Photographic Theater," in *Edgar Degas Photographer* (1998). She has also written significantly about twentieth-century photographers: "Like a Hot Iron Ball He Can Neither Swallow Nor Spit Out," in *Patrick Nagatani: Nuclear Enchantment* (1991); "Less of a Test Than Earth," in *Adam Fuss* (1997); "Convalescent . . . Incorruptible, Joel-Peter Witkin, Photographer" (1991), reprinted in *The Bone House* (1998). Among many awards, a Guggenheim (1973), and one from the American Council for Learned Societies (1980), a grant from the National Endowment for the Arts in literature (creative non-fiction) (1993) led to "A Hundred Different Stories," in *Photography's Multiple Roles . . .* (1998) where the author used photographs as points of departure for metafiction. The present publication is her first book to do the same. In 1987 she was decorated by the French government with the *Chevalier dans l'Ordre des Palmes académiques,* for contributions to the history of French art, based on *Degas Monotypes* (1968), which led many important artists to explore this medium. She taught the histories of art and photography at Wellesley College from 1968–1986, and at the University of New Mexico from 1987–1993. Eugenia Parry lives in Santa Fe, New Mexico.

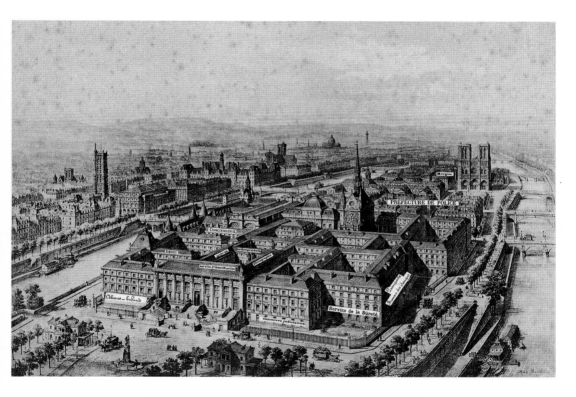

LOCATION OF THE SERVICE OF IDENTIFICATION

Bird's-eye view of the Palace of Justice and the Prefecture of Police in Paris

READING THE COLOR OF THE IRIS

6

Mensuration du pied.

MEASUREMENT OF THE FOOT

STUDIO OF PHOTOGRAPHY

CLASSIFICATION CUPBOARDS

The Album

A grey-eyed man is selling fossils in the Paris flea market. I approach. "Have any daguerreotypes?"

"But how did you know?" He gives me a strange look. Then asks if I'd like to meet his partner. We make an appointment. I go to a gallery of oriental antiquities on the Rue de Beaune. In the back is a cement floor, a space heater, and a library.

"You're ignorant about photography. We'll have to teach you."

They show me an album with a wrinkled green cloth cover that looks like it's been in a basement. There's nothing else special about it. They got it from *La Lanterne Magique,* a shop specializing in "curiosités, morbidités," on the Rue de Coétlogon. The proprietor, filthy, decadent and drunk, gave the album an outrageous price. He didn't want to sell. But they loved it so much. They kept coming back. Finally, he yielded, making them pay dearly.

I open the album and see it's full of old photographs. Brutal murders from the turn of the last century. Masses of women's hair, cut throats, dismembered torsos, sweating temples, morgue slabs, violated interiors disgorging debris. I cry out in protest. I've failed their test. They're jubilant.

For the next twenty-five years I never go to Paris without visiting the album. They let me take it to my furnished room where it sits on the table like a snake, indifferent, yet seeming to ask, "Are you something to eat?" I'm afraid to be in the same room with the thing. I place a spool of thread next to it, insisting on its ordinariness.

The photographs, inscribed and numbered in the negatives, come from the Paris police. They're beautiful. They make me sick. Each has an additional caption, pencil-written on plain grey pages. I peer at the scenes, hand to my face like a visor. I photograph the photographs, using the camera as a shield. I bring friends to see the album: "Nasty," they inform me.

I look at the album so long I know everyone in it like a member of my own family: Carrara, Pranzini, Petit Pierre, the Man Cut in Pieces. I take a photocopy of the album to the Paris police archives and ask where the other volumes are.

"There are no others. We don't keep our pictures this way."

"But who would assemble such a thing?"

"Someone inside, close to the police."

I imagine a miserably paid investigator, one of nameless hundreds, secretly pocketing pictures meant exclusively for the files, arranging them like gold under gaslight.

I read reports of the crimes in the Paris newspapers and copy surviving bits from police dossiers. All I get is facts. The pictures in the album say something else, ask me to separate the victims from the blood, to distinguish between the murderers' wild alibis. "This association, which tells me things about myself, would not suggest itself to another mind; mine cannot avoid it," Genet wrote in *The Thief's Journal*. I am Genet's thief.

Eugenia Parry

Come from the four winds, O breath,
and breathe upon these slain,
that they may live.

EZEKIEL 37:9

ALBUM: COLLECTION GÉRARD LÉVY, PARIS

Illustrations
pp. 5–13: Service d'identification (ed.), *Service d'identification,
Exposition universelle de Lyon 1897,* [Paris] 1897

pp. 16, 71, 85, 308: Archives historiques
de la Préfecture de Police, Paris

pp. 21, 23: Alphonse Bertillon,
La Photographie judiciaire, Paris 1890

pp. 311, 315: collection of the author

All other illustrations in this book stem from an untitled album
of crime photographs belonging to Gérard Lévy, Paris.

Eugenia Parry — Crime Album Stories
Editing: Alexis Schwarzenbach
Design: Hans Werner Holzwarth, Berlin
Scans: Gert Schwab / Steidl, Schwab Scantechnik, Göttingen
Printing: Steidl, Göttingen
© 2000: Eugenia Parry
© 2000 for this edition: Scalo Zurich – Berlin – New York
Head office: Weinbergstrasse 22a, CH-8001 Zurich / Switzerland,
phone 41 1 261 0910, fax 41 1 261 9262,
e-mail publishers@scalo.com, website www.scalo.com
Distributed in North America by D.A.P., New York City;
in Europe, Africa and Asia by Thames and Hudson, London;
in Germany, Austria and Switzerland by Scalo.

First Scalo Edition 2000
ISBN 3-908247-18-7
Printed in Germany

Contents

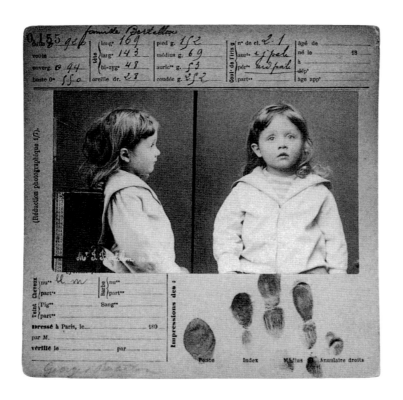

ANTHROPOMETRIC CARD
OF ALPHONSE BERTILLON'S NEPHEW GEORGES

1 My System

For me the capacity for logical methodology was predetermined by fate. I was six when one of my father's many scientific friends, Dr Letourneau, an anthropologist and amateur phrenologist, ran his hands over the bumps on my skull and announced to my family that I, Alphonse Bertillon, stutterer, obstinate weakling and sniveling tongue chewer, was not only predisposed to meticulousness, but destined to classify and create systems. But how could this occur since I refused to do any work?

I was a belligerent dunce, "The Barbarian," in a family of brilliant savants. My maternal grandfather, Achille Guillard, an eminent statistician, introduced my father, Louis-Adolphe Bertillon, a physician, to demography—and mesology, the science of milieus. My father made a patient study of human statistics, but his passion was mushrooms, a life-long labor. These scrupulous measurers, priests of a cult I barely grasped, were joined by others. The great brain specialist, Dr Broca, used big compasses to compare the skulls and bones of Australian aborigines and New Caledonian cannibals. The colleagues conducted their descriptive rituals with mesmerizing whispers, taking minute and concise notes. On my birth certificate under the rubric "Religion," my father wrote boldly, "None." He was already practicing his own: the patient and deliberate advancement of science.

I wish I could say I was inspired to emulate these paragons. Plagued by nosebleeds, migraines, a nervous stomach—how could I concentrate? My brothers and I were sent away to school, but I was expelled for throwing a book at a comrade. Later I practically martyred the poor, myopic German hired to tutor me at home.

I was twenty-six when I entered the administration of the Prefecture of Police in 1879. I'd done military service and worked in England tutoring children, with disastrous results. I did acquire English which allowed me to discover the genius of A. Conan Doyle and the elusive psyche of Edgar Allan Poe. These writers invented Sherlock Holmes and C. Auguste Dupin, two astounding sleuths, whose powers of observation bordered on the uncanny. It was comforting to realize how imperfect their natures were, that their prodigious deductions stemmed from a kind of malady of nerves.

I wanted to be a man of science. But my education was so fragmented, so lacking in discipline — Holmes and Dupin suffered from the same gaps. At the prefecture I was hired to copy and recopy cards. I also took courses in craniology, ethnology, and demography at the Ecole anthropologique where my father taught. And I wrote *Les Races sauvages* in 1882, a book of popular science.

The cards I copied for the Paris police contained descriptions of criminals in no perceivable order. Impossible to classify, there was little hope of using them to retrieve anyone. Besides, much of the information was dubious, provided by informers, or based on a prisoner's inevitably false testimony. There were also 60,000 photographs of prisoners, exposed in every conceivable light. How could we possibly link them to all the people arrested daily in Paris?

Late in 1879 I was fed up, obsessed to create my own order among these disturbing variables. I wrote reports about how to logically take and organize vital statistics, but none of my superiors would listen. Louis Andrieux, Prefect of Police, deciding I was a fantasist, threatened to fire me. But I pointed out that his own dossier was a mire of statistical nonsense. Even his birth date was wrong.

I'd done a metric study of each of the bones of the human skeleton while in the military. I recalled the serene atmosphere of statistical measurement in my parents' house, where everyone discussed the work of the great Belgian scholar, Quételet, the first to show that mathematical rules dominate the mysterious distribution of forms and dimensions in nature, who created a statistical curve to demonstrate this.

I devised a simple, elegant system called anthropometry. It was a revolution in measuring human beings and establishing each person's uniqueness through numbers. Nature doesn't proceed in jumps, and no language expresses what numbers can of human gradations. In 1882, my new boss, Camescasse, understood my potential. He gave me two assistants and three months to establish this system and show how it could identify a repeat offender. We measured 589 suspects, of which I was able to identify 49 recidivists. By 1888 I had a Department of Judicial Identity on the upper floors of the Palais de Justice. Made chief in 1894, I had five million cards arranged in my cabinets (women and minors: one million, separated from the men: four million).

My wife, Amélie, wrote out more than 7,000 of these cards. I married her for two things: her tiny, perfect, white teeth and her impeccable handwriting. We first met on the Rue de Rivoli because, wearing thick glasses, she couldn't see to cross the street. Soon she was giving me German lessons. It wasn't a romance from my point of view. I'd fallen hopelessly in love when I was younger — enough heartache for a lifetime.

Amélie is small, pink, and very blond. Never interested in the currents of fashion that enslave *la parisienne,* her dresses are the colors of a carnival. And her hats, where flora and effigies of fauna gather, are, how to say it politely? They're ... Austrian. Nonetheless, I'd found the perfect ally and collaborator. Amélie worshipped me. Called me a genius before I believed I was one.

Anthropometry measures bones. I based its logic on three indisputable facts: after the age of twenty, human bones are nearly absolutely fixed; from one person to another, there is extreme diversity in the skeleton; and it's easy to measure a live subject precisely with a simple ruler and sliding compass. These measurements can easily be retrieved through a precise filing system, no matter how many cards accumulate. Any policeman of ordinary intelligence can do it.

From nine every morning, some 100 men and women, detained by the police, climbed a spiral staircase to my Department of Anthropometry. In the measuring room we had them disrobe (down to trousers and shirt — women retained their dresses) and remove their shoes and stockings. Which was necessary for the procedure, but I'd also calculated its psychological effect. No violator of the law, whom I can get barefooted, is capable of the same brutality as when he's shod. Because even barbarians are highly sensitive to decorum, I instructed my assistants to have them be seated, another technique that achieves submission. With utmost courtesy my staff would discuss the weather, being forbidden to mention the detainee's crime or progress of his case.

We took ten measurements: height; length of arms outstretched (there's a well-known correlation between these two — the latter usually being four centimeters greater than the former); torso height; length and width of head and right ear; length of the left foot; distance between left elbow and middle finger; and length of the middle finger. We called out the numbers to two registrars, surveying the proceedings from desks raised on platforms, who inscribed them on a special card. Simplicity itself, the whole process took about seven minutes. Converted into numbers, the person was not only ours, he could be retrieved again and again, whether he'd changed his name, weight, clothing, profession, added a tattoo, or suffered a scar. Specialists, combing my cabinets by a process of elimination, could find anyone in five minutes.

What matters in retrieving a criminal is "the quality of the observation," of knowing "what to observe," as Poe wrote in "The Murders in the Rue Morgue," a classic of deduction. Noting, in addition, peculiar body marks — moles, tattoos, scars — and eye color in clear northern light, I calculated that the chances of these eleven statistics recurring in more than one individual were over four million to one.

Which is why I was tyrannical when it came to order and discipline. The least error could be catastrophic. Discovering carelessness,

RAOUL PHOTOGRAPHED DURING HIS FIRST ARREST,
NOVEMBER 1884

I was merciless. Lazy assistants hated my cold stare, but those who obeyed revered me all their lives. My system was infallible because I was incorruptible, which limited the number of my friends. Forced into isolation, I researched even more deeply the chaos of humanity. My satisfaction came from knowing that police departments world-wide were adopting my methods.

Music-hall singers warbled about anthropometry, calling it *le bertillonage*. The publicity embarrassed me. Worse, these entertainers were alerting those against whom I directed my work. Criminals thought they could disappear into obscurity. With my beacon on them, their rage knew no bounds. Visiting the prisons I endured taunts and obscene gestures. Unsigned letters threatened my life. Frightened, Amélie begged to accompany me to the prefecture. I said I'd be my own watchdog.

Anthropometry wasn't my only weapon against malefactors. I was also regularly using photography. After the measuring room, sub-jects proceeded to a sky-lighted studio on the top floor. Because of my systematization of their measurements, I had to create an equally fool-proof way of photographing them that corroborated the numbers. Photography is exact, but susceptible to many variables. The kind of photograph that would serve any case had to be brutally realistic. We may think we know someone by looking at him, but we're only remembering movements and gestures. We've rarely scrutinized the immobile face. I photographed the suspect seated, front and right side, simultaneously, one-fifth natural size, unretouched, and added these two images to his anthropometric card.

The reliability of this method may be illustrated by the case of young Raoul. First arrested in November 1884, the boy meekly submitted to my lens. By his second arrest in 1885, he'd been con-verted to the street, calling himself "Billardo." Six months of criminal activity had changed his psychology profoundly. Distracted by his twisted grimace, an untrained eye would hardly know it was the same boy. But we'd made both images in exactly the same light, which

RAOUL PHOTOGRAPHED DURING HIS SECOND ARREST,
MAY 1885

allowed us to see through the differing states of his soul to the fact that the profiles and ears in both images matched, revealing his anthropometry, the real truth of him.

If someone balked at this photographic phase, and many did, especially the anarchists, we never protested. "Come back when you're feeling more comfortable," we'd say. But as we led them back to their cell, a camera mounted on the corridor wall exploded a flash, freezing the suspects in a completely natural pose.

My successes, regularly published in the newspapers, made me so famous that in 1894 I was called as an expert in the Dreyfus Affair, for I'd also begun analyzing handwriting. With the arrest of Captain Alfred Dreyfus, the Jew charged with high treason, came another chance to demonstrate my powers. I don't hate Jews. They're brilliant scientists. I responded to the call of duty, though no one believed it. I had to be an anti-Semite to say what I did.

I proved Dreyfus guilty beyond a shadow of a doubt. The memorandum or *bordereau,* he was thought to have written, a key piece of incriminating evidence in the government's case, suggested he was passing military secrets to the Germans. The Penal Code, Article 76, specifically states, "Whosoever will have engaged in machinations or shared information with foreign powers ... will be punished by death."

It was clear to me. Only Dreyfus could have written the memorandum. It was on thin onionskin paper. People forge plenty of documents to cause the downfall of a personal enemy. I thought he might have traced the memorandum from another document. I declared that he'd forged his own writing, imitating, not spontaneously, but geometrically, in shifts, displacements, and deviations, that of his own, his brother's, and his wife's script, combined, so he could claim the document was fabricated and deny any resemblance to his own hand since he'd imitated it. Preposterous? I didn't think so. Even though it meant the guillotine for him. At the trial I presented charts and diagrams, all connecting his tricks as the network of an inveterate and professional traitor. It was a masterpiece of deduction. It stripped Dreyfus bare.

Jean Casimir-Périer, President of the Republic, heard me out in two separate sessions and concluded I was "compulsively rational . . . , truly insane." Dreyfus himself thought my work "mad." That meant little to me. Dealing with criminals we assume twisted habits to match their own. The other experts contradicted each other. Only my interpretation was irrefutable, absolute. Dreyfus had led a double life. Detesting public speaking, I nearly collapsed at the blackboard. Everyone was laughing. Crucified for what they called my "delirium," I was furious. "After my death," I told them, "I'll be judged by history."

* * *

I should add that another refinement of my method was that I decided that scenes of crimes, especially violent ones, needed to be documented with my characteristic precision. Happily, no one regarded this as "delirious." The messes people make in killing each other is one thing. But when we, who are supposed to make sense of them are as chaotic as the murderers, that's judicial decadence. Sherlock Holmes expressed it with characteristic impatience: "How simple it would have been had I arrived before they wallowed all over it like a herd of buffalo!" That was crime-scene procedure before I came along. I realized how important it is to have photographs of these morbid aftermaths. Mostly, to show the jury so they would convict. Anyone viewing the obscenity of murder can do nothing else. Sometimes a crime-scene photograph, and I made elegant ones, is unnecessary because of more compelling factors that solve a case. But at the outset, how do we know this? Besides, all of these photographs tell a story.

2   Big Pink Boy

16–17 March 1887, 17 Rue Montaigne,
VIIIth Arrondissement, Marie Regnault, 39,
courtesan, Annette Gremeret,
(age unknown) her chamber maid,
and Marie-Louise Gremeret, 11, the maid's
presumed daughter, hacked to death with
a machete by Henri-Jacques-Ernest Pranzini,
31, thief, embezzler, gambler. Sentenced
to death by guillotine 13 July 1887.
Executed 31 August 1887.

I'm Godinet. I had zero for a future till I came to Paris and got lucky. Me seventeen, no experience, and I'm hired by Dr Poirier, one of the anatomy chiefs at the Faculty of Medicine.

It was stinking bad. Most kids would've run screaming when Poirier gave them the knife and said, start cutting. They'd rather make lousy tips waiting tables. I was knee-high in gore, but it made me famous.

We always needed fresh bodies. Most were unknowns, murder victims or poor souls who died in the street and went unclaimed at the morgue. My job was stripping the skin so Poirier could examine them for science. He had his theories. I helped supply the evidence.

We also got the ones who lost their heads under the blade of "The Widow," the guillotine, famous assassins written up in the papers.

Poirier and his doctors were greedy for their brains. They thought something special in their size or shape would show mysterious, twisted things regular people didn't have. I wasn't in on that part. Poirier'd crack the head himself and take the brain to look at in private.

I was busy. Wading in muscle and fat. One hundred and fifty bodies a year. We gave some to taxidermists who soaked them in chemicals and gave us back clean skeletons for the students to study. My parents were proud, me at the faculty. I couldn't explain it was worse than a meat market.

I never felt any sorrow. The bodies weren't people, just things I got paid to cut up. I'd stare at a dead face, but it wasn't looking back at me. It was having its own thoughts. That's what happens. You don't feel anything. There are so many.

I'd notice when a body was young. In the beginning I wondered about the ones my age. But that stopped. I'd just feel bad when I thought I could have ended up like that, dead before my time.

Hacking and stripping. The job got pretty monotonous, so anything out of the ordinary would get me excited. A hand without a thumb. A tattoo with a bleeding heart, or a name. I'd keep the hand a while. Or wrap up the tattooed skin to look at on my own. I showed them to a girl I met in a wine shop. Took her to an alley and opened my handkerchief under a street lamp. She was plenty scared. Too scared to tell the police. After the fun, I took my souvenirs back to the garbage.

Medical students'd come and ask for women's breasts to make tobacco pouches. They wanted skulls framed with a bone or two from a famous killer, something for their mantelpieces to impress their girlfriends. I understood.

I knew all the students. They were my age. Sniveling runts, I thought, but they had prestige. One day they'd be making a pile. For the moment I had the power. I made them beg for my bits and pieces. They wanted them so much. Lots of people on the inside did.

Pranzini. Assassin de Marie Regnault, sa bonne et la fille de sa bonne

Marie Regnault *Annette Gremeret (la bonne)* *Marie Gremeret (fille de la bonne)*

PRANZINI, MURDERER OF MARIE REGNAULT, HER MAID, AND THE MAID'S DAUGHTER

Marie Regnault; Annette Gremeret (the maid); Marie Gremeret (the maid's daughter)

They had their reasons. I didn't ask. A tattoo or a hand without a thumb could be interesting. I started thinking. There's money to be made here. The whole city's filled with poor people living off what no one wants. Look at the rag-and-bone men in the XXth Arrondissement. Their caravans are piles of junk. All their lives they're chewing throwaways.

I didn't sell right off. That was my wish. But I found out I was *expected* to trade in these goods. No one said so, but I got word it was a tradition. It's hard to explain when you're not on the inside, the desire, I had it, too, to keep certain scraps.

People'd stand around and watch. Medical students, agents from criminal investigation, ordinary policemen wandered in, curious. One'd approach and say, "How about a souvenir?" A skull, some skin from a notorious cut-throat, maybe a button from his breeches? They were quiet about it. It wasn't just these people wanting things for free. There were paying customers. Respectable ladies arrived, as if they were shopping at a bazaar, and asked for something they could make into a brooch. One came after an execution so she could add the criminal's skull to her collection. She offered a lot for the skulls of his victims, too. Campi? The guy who killed the old man and his sister? He had a huge torso. A gentleman had a piece of his skin made into a book cover. I'm not naming names, but a former chief of criminal investigation still uses a criminal's skull as an inkwell.

It was understood. Investigators and judiciaries liked these things. Maybe they brought them luck. I don't think so. It was curiosity. A way of making their miserable lives a little more exciting. Their pay was pitiful. Mine too. What was disgusting to everyone else was magic to us.

First off, I thought of the money. But with exotic goods to sell I was in a special society. I was in demand. I didn't know what Poirier was doing on the side. Maybe the same thing, but I ended up taking the heat.

It all blew up with Prànzini. After his head fell in the basket we got him in two pieces. Pranzini was a celebrity, one of the most fantastic murderers Paris ever saw. He took a machete and slaughtered a high-priced courtesan, her maid, and the maid's little girl. All that was left alive were Dick and Lili, two pug dogs who hid under a couch. The press published thousands of details, plus a map of the courtesan's apartment, and they made sly comments about some sexual devices they found in her night table.

Henri Pranzini was an Italian from Egypt. He was sleeping with Marie Regnault. In her world she was called Régine de Montille. She was like all those women who sleep with the high and low. She bragged about her jewels and piles of money. So Pranzini goes in, pays for his pleasure, and slashes her throat so he can take the francs, rings, bracelets, and watches. The maid wakes up. He kills her too. He looks around for witnesses, finds the maid's little daughter sleeping and finishes her off.

His strength was tremendous. His concentration was written all over the bodies. Their hearts kept pumping blood even after they were dead. It was a mess made by a slaughtering genius. Blood everywhere.

Bertillon took photographs of the victims at the morgue. He took Pranzini's three dead females close up. Excellent work. He got the hacked shoulder and cut throat of Marie Regnault. Her long hair flowed over the morgue slab. Her eyes were wide open. You could see the terror. Bertillon took the maid, to show how Pranzini nearly decapitated her, and the little girl with the worse wound of all. Only a piece of skin held her head to her neck. The pictures circulated in the offices. They were very well done. Everyone wanted them.

Police archivists used to make presentations of spectacular crimes with Bertillon's pictures. They hung them in little displays at the prefecture. Pranzini's case was a prime candidate. The victims, shown dead and alive, were artistically arranged, attached to the mountings with silk ribbons. Fancy writing identified everyone involved. In one frame you had the crime in a nutshell.

Plenty of photographs of the case were floating around. People in the morgue and police agents fought over everything about Pranzini and his victims. In the apartment the police found pictures of the courtesan dressed for a ball with her hair powdered, or like an Amazon for horseback riding. How saucy she'd looked to all the gentlemen who paid for her favors.

A picture of her maid Annette Gremeret showed a timid thing. Everyone wanted her, too, because of all the women Marie Regnault knew, Annette was her closest friend. There was even more magic in the little girl, Marie-Louise, who had the first name of the whore and the last name of the maid. Everyone suspected she was the courtesan's love child. "See how she resembles Regnault? She doesn't look anything like Annette." She's holding a doll. Her eyes have that flirty brightness of the lady of the place where she was being raised. She was about to take her first communion. A prayer book was found by her body. We also learned about Marie Regnault's will. The little girl was chief inheritor, before the courtesan's own parents! This confirmed our suspicions. All this intrigue made their pictures especially interesting to have.

* * *

After the crime, Pranzini escaped by train to Marseilles and went to a whore house where he showed off, giving the girls the stolen jewels. The whores smelled death. They fluttered like hens when a fox is in the coop. They showed the *flics* their presents, which matched those on an official list of Marie Regnault's possessions. Pranzini was grabbed in Marseilles. He wanted to be caught. For a guy so smart, why did he hang on to the stuff and give it to whores, who always snitch?

When they got Pranzini to Paris, Bertillon measured every bit of him. He was a trophy. Not an ordinary murderer. The Christian brothers in Egypt had given him an education. He spoke five languages. His whole life he was fooling people. He worked the Pullman cars, stealing passengers' money. He won and lost in gaming rooms all over the world. He liked older women and used his affectionate nature to take advantage of their weaknesses.

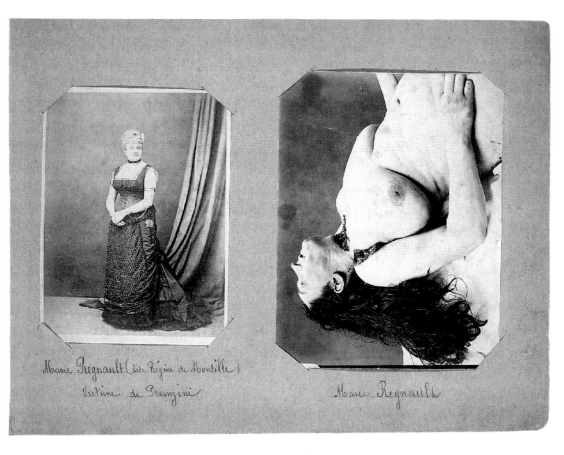

MARIE REGNAULT (CALLED RÉGINE DE MONTILLE)

Victim of Pranzini

The *flics* were impressed by Pranzini's strong head and bull's neck. He had huge muscles in his arms and shoulders, compared to weak legs and thighs. He'd been in the Sudan wars, interpreting for the British army. He had seen plenty of violence there, so we weren't surprised he had used a huge knife for his crime, the kind hunters have to cut up deer or wild boar. They photographed him, front and side, showing him as a brute. One of the pictures they used for display was him standing with a bunch of agents. They were smiling. One held a big knife. It wasn't his. He'd thrown the murder weapon away. They borrowed another one for the picture.

Scientists held a measuring rod to his sexual parts. They were unusually large. When we got him in the morgue, I saw Pranzini was a bull at stud. His body was big, pink, and blond. He looked like a hog butcher.

Pranzini, dead, was prime material. His future was in my hands. Rossignol, one of the best detectives, watched us do the autopsy. He took me aside, "My boss Goron has no souvenir of this big, pink boy. He wants something to remember him by. How about a button from his trousers?" Pranzini was in twenty pieces. I was going to gather him up and send him to the cemetery. "We've got no buttons. The pants and shirt are at the annex," I said. "Take a piece of skin and make a purse."

Rossignol liked my idea. He was ready for anything. That's how he caught people no one else could. He took a piece from the Pranzini heap, a nice slice from the left breast. A journalist already had an ear, another a finger, another a lip, and so on. Me, I'd taken his thighs to the tanner's.

I wasn't going to do Rossignol's work for him. He was as clever as me. He took the skin home and heated it. He stripped off the muscle and got rid of the fat, soaking it in alum astringent, like taxidermists do, which made it dry and hard. It was white and quite thick, he said. He massaged it all day till it became wondrously supple, soft as butter.

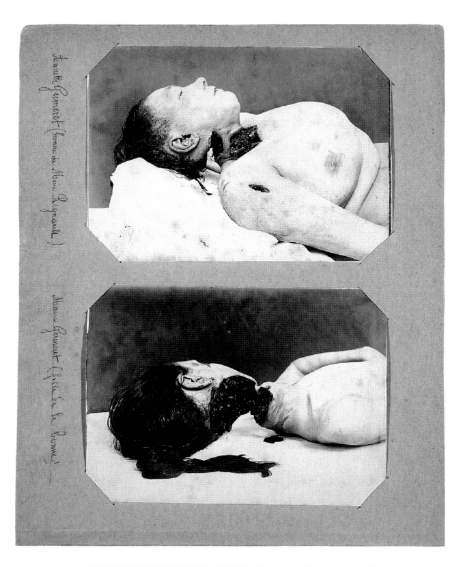

ANNETTE GREMERET (MAID OF MARIE REGNAULT)

Marie Gremeret (daughter of the maid)

He looked in the Bottin directory for a leather worker who wasn't thick with the police. He instructed him to make two calling card cases. He wanted three, but there wasn't enough. "Funny. This white, hairy flesh. What animal is it?" Rossignol didn't say. He just watched while the leather worker passed his tongue over the skin.

It cost him twenty francs to get the card cases. They were lined with blue satin. Rossignol was so happy, he couldn't keep his mouth shut. "You just sewed the skin of Pranzini!" That was his mistake.

He gave one case to Assistant Chief of Criminal Investigation Goron. "I only wanted a button!" He gave the other to Goron's boss, Chief of Criminal Investigation Taylor. Taylor, a gentleman, didn't dare refuse the gift. He didn't want to seem to assign blame, since Goron'd already accepted one for himself. Taylor tried to get rid of his case. He offered it to the Prefect of Police, who was revolted. The maker of the cases blabbed the story to *Le Figaro,* which exposed the scandal in several articles.

It was all over Paris. A crime worse than Pranzini's. You want butchers? Man-eaters? Look to the police! No one inside was surprised. Taylor's predecessor, Macé, had his own private criminal museum. He wrote a book with illustrations of his collection of murder weapons and assassins' neckerchiefs. So many people had things all members of French police would have to be investigated.

Everyone attacked Rossignol for violating the sanctity of Pranzini's grave. What grave? This detective only stooped to pick up what was on the floor of my theater. Goron had to appear before the Procurer of the Republic, who ordered him to throw both cases into the fireplace. They watched, holding their noses, while the flames cooked the skin and stank up the office.

A police commissioner was told to go to the taxidermist's and get back Pranzini's thighs. Taylor was forced to retire. Goron got his job. Professor Poirier wasn't blamed, but I was fired. On my way up north I wondered what to tell my parents. I was a household name. I was grateful Rossignol kept his mouth shut about my other trading. Whoever went to the tanner's for Pranzini's thighs would find the thighs of a negro I was getting treated to make myself some bedroom slippers.

3   Nobodies

14 January 1886, 52 Rue de Caumartin,
IXth Arrondissement, Marie-Camille Aguétant,
28, courtesan, murdered with a razor by Prado,
called Louis-Charles-Frédéric, Count de Linska
de Castillón, 28, adventurer, gambler,
pimp, journalist, thief. Condemned to death
14 November 1888. Executed by guillotine
27 December 1888.

Marie-Camille Aguétant went through maids like she went through the men who filed into her apartment and paid 500 francs a night to mount her, spend themselves, and snore like walruses in her bed. The maids and clients stayed as long as they were useful. Then she threw them out. As for her patron Jules Blès, a croupier at the Franco-American casino who kept her in a small third-floor flat on the Rue de Caumartin, he was a fixture who'd learned his place. His most important contribution to Marie's scheme of things was keeping out of her way. Jules would arrive after three in the morning to be sure and miss the last visitor. It was his little courtesy. In their arrangement, Marie gave Jules what he needed in the way of sexual favors but found him a bore. Too obliging, she thought. As for loving him, the suggestion would have made her laugh.

Marie-Camille Aguétant didn't love anyone. But she did love one thing. This was a three-tiered diamond necklace, which circled her throat in a blaze of icy brilliance. She adored the necklace for the mystery of its coldness, its imperious resistance to her will. The necklace became her ally and trademark. She wore it strolling through the lobby of the Eden Theater and among the tables of the Café Américain. With her diamonds exploding into life against the gaslight chandeliers and gigantic mirrors, Marie-Camille Aguétant, known as "Madame Camille," commanded the crowd.

Madame Camille had the body of a low-class whore. Like the notorious courtesans of the Second Empire who were her idols, she waged a constant battle to conceal her true shape. Lacking wit or humor, her trick in public was to dazzle with fine toilettes. In the bedroom she tinted her sallow flesh with the glow of firelight or flaming candelabras. She counted on her dressmaker to work magic on her crab's torso, stumpy legs, and breasts that began to collapse before her twenty-eighth birthday.

A hairdresser used combs to snag her thinning hair into shining coils and a curling iron to frizz it, unfortunately exposing bald spots. But the effect softened the slit of a mouth and grasping expression. Cunningly caked with rice powder, Madame Camille entered the Eden and the Café Américain a tricked-up mongrel and emerged a celebrity. Her tiny, compact form led to another epithet. Everyone at the Eden called her "La Crevette" (The Shrimp).

The Shrimp's favorite topic of conversation was her money. She would insinuate, in stage whispers, that there was more where her finery came from. Her acquaintances, for few really knew her, remembered tedious descriptions of other jewels and intimations of a fortune. Besides the fabulous necklace, this amounted only to assorted trinkets: a blue enameled watch, diamond earrings, and some 6,000 francs in cash, hidden in red leather pouches in a mirrored armoire. There she also squirreled away stock certificates and government shares worth around 25,000 francs. Compared to the great courtesans like Cora Pearl, who amassed millions during spectacular careers and thought nothing of pissing away 30,000 francs on a bad night at baccarat, Marie's hoard was a pittance. Yet to her it must have seemed grand — her father lived in a home for beggars in Lyons.

Among her clients were tourists who came to the pleasure spots of the Café Américain and the Eden, with its Hindu-pagoda décor on the Rue Boudreau, looking for sex with the perfect French whore. Marie provided the immodest pleasures they expected to find in Paris. She was so smartly turned out that she appeared to the newcomer as practically respectable, at least in gaslight. Besides, it was an easy walk from these places to her apartment.

Oscar Wilde, triumphant from his American lecture tour, fucked Marie Aguétant early in 1883, and even wrote down her name. Spotting her at the Eden, he escorted her to the Rue de Caumartin and paid his 500 francs: "What animals we are," he grieved afterward, and confessed humping a prostitute was like "chewing cold mutton." When his friend Robert Sherard worried Oscar might have been robbed by such monsters, the playwright cried, "One gives them all that is in one's pockets!" Which was exactly what Marie had in mind.

* * *

Late in 1885 a more complicated stranger began to meet Marie Aguétant at the Eden. He was twenty-eight, Spanish, and affected the air of a courtier by speaking impeccable French. Sloe-eyed, and brutally built, ready to burst from a jacket buttoned to hide the fact that he had no shirt, he presented a vain image by having his hair cut in a fashionable Nero-coif, which Oscar Wilde also affected in Paris. But this foreigner's presumption was a kind of malady, expressed through cold, calculating silences which hid, not altogether successfully, a rampant imagination and a passion for gambling. He looked the flamboyant *espagnol,* but no one knew his real name or what he did for a living. When pressed, he said he was a broker or journalist, but regular work repelled him. Actually, he was a high-class pirate with the cleverness of a gypsy. His main occupations were robbery and murder, which he performed to enhance his reputation at roulette.

At twenty he led of a band of brigands that ravaged the Antilles. Boarding a Spanish steamer at Puerto Plata in the Dominican Republic he put a bullet into the head of the captain while his accomplices fleeced the passengers. Some said the attack was part of the Cuban rebellion, and his men were stealing food for the insurgents. It was grist for gossips. Since he was also rumored to be the illegitimate son of the President of Peru, at the Eden he became "The American" and for several months pursued the Shrimp.

He didn't give Marie everything in his pockets. What he stole he spent on roulette. Theft was only one source of cash for the devilish numbers on red or black. He also capitalized on stunning skills at making women fall in love with him. While getting to know Marie he maintained a stable of thieving prostitutes who were kept busy filling his wallet with money, which disappeared like quicksilver when his bets failed. His voice was a musical caress, so beguiling, so persuasive that though he was not really handsome, women found him irresistibly attractive. Each member of his fold considered him her exclusive fancy man.

When he met Marie-Camille Aguétant he was living with a golden-eyed, curly-haired blonde of twenty-three named Eugénie Forestier, whom he'd lured away from her husband to become a common whore. He introduced her to an American businessman, and dictated compromising letters which he forced her to send to extort money from him. He'd already grabbed money from dozens of women, many older than himself, who fed on his murmurs of undying love. In the little prank with Eugénie he called himself Haro, which he said was his mother Esperanza's maiden name. Hypnotized by the Spaniard, Eugénie, who considered herself his wife, became Madame Haro.

He had other names. Sometimes he was Rohoro de Mendoza. Or Stanislas, for he claimed to be half-Polish. Or Stanislas Prado y Ribo, for he sometimes gave the names of his parents as Stanislas Prado and Esperanza Ribo. Or he was the Count de Prado. A favorite

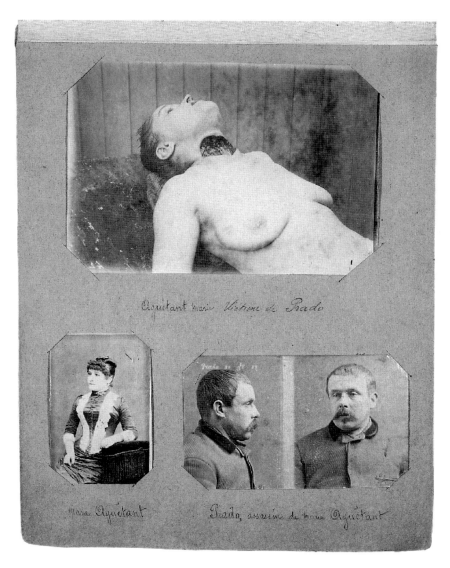

AGUÉTANT, MARIE, VICTIM OF PRADO

Marie Aguétant; Prado, murderer of Marie Aguétant

name he invented to mystify the crowds at the casinos, and which he signed on photographs he gave to ready mistresses, was Count Louis-Charles-Frédéric de Linska de Castillón. Later, to the police, he was simply Prado.

He had already abandoned a wife in Madrid, Dolores Garces y Marcilla whom he married in 1879. After depleting her dowry of 170,000 francs, he forced her into prostitution and tried to poison her. While she was pregnant, he made her drink iced water and beat her to a pulp. She was later discovered living in penury in a Madrid attic as the Countess de Linska de Castillón.

* * *

Given the various women who'd sacrificed themselves to him, Marie Aguétant, with all her airs, was no one special, just a blabbering fool who seemed fabulously rich. With proper handling she would become another source of money. By late 1885, he began wheedling his way into her life. He didn't ply her with exaggerated compliments. He could hardly lead her into prostitution. She was already a specialist.

To seduce Marie he became humble and submissive. He'd appear at the Rue de Caumartin while she was with her dressmaker and sit for hours, breathing adenoidally through a gaping mouth, which he took trouble to conceal under a thick mustache. He'd watch her being stuffed like sausage into yards of burgundy satin edged in lace. In this setting he called himself "Monsieur Emile." Marie's maid Rosalie nicknamed him "Le Petit Gris," partly to demean this parasite, but also because his pale grey suit distinguished him from her mistress's other hangers-on.

For several months Prado, prone to cruelty when things fouled up, became a model of patience. He had a tough opponent in the wily prostitute. It was a gamble, but games of chance were his life, all the more intriguing when the stakes were women with money. He would arrive at the apartment three or four times a week around dinner time, chewing on a toothpick to look as if he'd just eaten. In truth, he was ravenous. Besides, he knew his regular appearance at table would soften his hostess, a lonely calculator like himself. He enthralled her with stories of fabulous adventures in Mozambique, Calcutta, Hong Kong, Haiti, Havana, Lisbon, San Francisco, and New York. He told her about a gambling house he owned in Madrid where he had used a rigged roulette board to rob a bunch of Greeks of 200,000 francs. "It was legitimate," he whispered *sotto voce*. "I was robbing thieves!" At which Marie's beady eyes glittered like jet.

The Spaniard also peppered his courtship with certain perversities. He refused to pay for her sexual services. Nor did he tip the maid. This effrontery, he figured, not only forced the whore to break her rules; it had the deeper effect of confusing her. Here he was practically living off her, and she didn't get rid of him. What she wouldn't admit was that she found his undermining of her authority fascinating, sexually exciting, even admirable. Her "American" was dashing, mercenary, cool, a stylish aristocrat, a man of the world—utterly devastating. Her reverence for him was not unlike what she felt toward her imperious diamonds. Little by little, she became his collaborator against herself.

There was nothing simple in the liaison. Marie hurled insults. She loved laughing at him, which hid the fact that she had yielded. She choreographed their battles to focus on money he didn't have so she could make him feel small and powerless, as she herself had come to feel in his presence. In these spats the blood would rush to his face. He felt like shooting her on the spot. Mastering himself, he'd beam, beatifically, with what the maid called "the head of a Jesuit." Once when he made a pass at the maid, which was strictly from boredom since he found her intolerably plain, Marie made a jealous scene and put him out. Soon after, the maid left.

* * *

45

The Spaniard decided to lower the curtain on the dalliance with Aguétant when in early 1886 Eugénie had to borrow twenty francs from the keeper of the hotel where she and Prado lived to get her winter cloak from the pawnbroker. The affair was eating up time. Besides, he suspected the treasure in her armoire was probably not all she claimed. On the night of 14 January he took Eugénie to a friend's house, saying he was dining out and would return late. Then he went to the Eden and around ten-thirty left with the Shrimp.

At her flat, they went into the bedroom. Marie undressed. Babette, the new maid, didn't know the visitor but remarked he was wearing a grey overcoat and hid his face under a stylish square-brimmed hat. As she changed the bed she thought it strange that he remained in shadow, away from the lamp. He also never took his hands from his pockets. Babette asked if they wanted anything more, then took her post in the kitchen.

At the bidet in a thin chemise, Marie began her whining sarcasm, "And how much will you give me tonight, *chéri*?" To which he exploded, "Nothing!" And pounced. An open razor flashed. He grabbed her hair and cut her throat. Then he broke into the armoire and sliced the red leather pouches. "Only 6,000 francs?" he whimpered, stuffing the bills, diamond necklace, and other jewels into his coat. Barricading the chamber with the bed, he took a lighted candle and left by another door, passing Babette, asleep in a chair. He ran downstairs and rapped on the window of the concierge, who was so used to Aguétant's flow of night visitors that he pulled the door cord, and without a word, let the murderer leave.

Jules Blès returned from the casino around three. Babette blocked the bedroom. "Madame is with a *Monsieur*!" Blès forced the door, shoving the bed aside. In the firelight the croupier saw his mistress astride the bidet, a dead flower, petals wide open, breasts drooping. Her shift was a pile on the floor. She looked almost beautiful with her eyes gazing into infinity. When he raised her head, it fell away from his hands. Blood filling the basin overflowed and pooled under his shoes.

He looked in the armoire. The shares were undisturbed, but the red leather purses, slashed through, like Marie's throat, were gaping holes. Blès began to shake. He couldn't weep. He was too afraid.

Prado was also afraid. It was a new kind of fear. Sick to his stomach, he hurried through the January cold to the room he shared with Eugénie. In his plunders he always used a pistol, a Bulldog with a short barrel that struck hard. He liked to deliver mean blows from a safe distance. At Marie's he hadn't risked the noise. Embracing a woman half-naked in a dance of death, staring into her face, blue with terror, hearing her gasp, feeling her squirm while he used his own razor, revolted him to the core. It was too close. Her humid flesh was all over him.

To Eugénie he babbled all night about the murder of a whore, getting up ten times to wash his hands, which he said, "smelled bad." Next morning she watched him burn his shirt and cuffs. A rank odor in the stove turned out to be his smoldering shoes.

"Why?" she asked.

"Because I choose to."

When she noticed that a hundred-franc bill he gave her was sliced he took it back and gave her another. He explained his not shaving, "I've taken my razor to be sharpened." He left and returned wearing a dark suit, saying he'd given the grey one to someone in the street.

In a restaurant, he spoke to her of nothing but the murder of the whore on the Rue de Caumartin which the newspapers were broadcasting as the latest Paris sensation. He even joked about it. "That's one woman fewer. I'd like to rid the world of the whole lot!" Seeing that this disturbed his mistress, he cried, "Calm down! She was a nobody!"

Marie-Camille Aguétant was buried in the Saint-Ouen cemetery on 3 February. Her father left his misery in Lyons to attend the funeral, then moved into her apartment to live like a lord. Her murderer, the inscrutable Prado, had been careful to leave no traces to link him to the crime. But finding himself blathering about the whore, lying about his clothes, trying to conceal razor-slashed money, he blurted out to his mistress what he'd done. He regretted this moment of weakness. "No woman should have that kind of power. I'll have to kill her too."

* * *

Prado left for Spain, saying he needed to sell some land. In Madrid he sold Marie's diamonds to a hag at a jeweler's, *Plata y Pedrería,* at 2 Ciudad Rodrigo, and seduced her daughter, a beauty called Purita. As a souvenir of their ephemeral amour, he gave the girl his photograph, in which she noticed a decoration on his jacket identifying him as the Count de Linska de Castillón.

Eugénie joined him—he decided he was stuck with her—and they went to live in Bordeaux. Maybe they worried about the police, but no one bothered them. There Prado made love to Mauricette Couronneau, a pretty brunette of seventeen, daughter of the owner of their hotel. When Mauri, for whom this union was a supreme passion, became pregnant and bore him a daughter, he tried to leave Eugénie. But she tore her clothes and threatened to tell everything. He decided to finish her. "Like you did the whore?" she taunted. He attacked her with a knife. But she grabbed it from his hand and slipped it down a window sash. He aimed his revolver. The bullet missed, hitting the wall.

He didn't persist. Eugénie knew the worst, but he didn't care anymore. Having someone close to share in one clear truth about him was not only a relief, it was strangely stimulating. So he spent two years in Bordeaux between Eugénie and Mauri. He thought of Eugénie as an "evil wind" who cultivated in him the refinements of sexual passion. But Mauri was the love of his life. With that declaration, the girl began calling herself the Countess de Linska de Castillón.

To maintain a constant flow of cash for the casinos, the murderer of Marie Aguétant organized a band of seventy accomplices which ranged the south of France, stealing money and jewels. The police of

Bordeaux, Royan, Marennes, Arcachon, Bagnères-de-Luchon, Pau, Montpellier, Arles, Nîmes, Toulouse, Agen, Toulon, and Marseilles recorded these attacks and rounded up suspects, but there wasn't enough evidence to convict anyone. After two years Prado, weary of these provincial escapades, was hungry for big stakes. In November 1887, he abandoned Mauricette and returned to Paris with Eugénie to absorb himself in roulette's little ivory ball. As was his habit, he stayed alert for opportunities.

* * *

He learned that a certain Antoine Lorenzo, a Spanish dealer in gem stones, was staying on the right bank at the Hôtel du Palais. He checked in as Count de Linska de Castillón, taking a room next to Lorenzo's. He approached his compatriot with warm kindness, even presented him and his family with a complimentary box at the Châtelet Theater.

While the Lorenzos were safely at the performance, he entered their quarters from his neighboring room and broke the lock of Madame Lorenzo's trunk. Finding nothing, he panicked, grabbed a smaller chest, which his tools wouldn't open, and took it with him. He was curious to know what was inside. Flaunting his prize, he demanded a waiter call him a cab. "That chest isn't part of *your* luggage, Monsieur."

Prado bolted into the street. Several waiters chased him down the Quai de la Conférence. At the Pont des Invalides he dropped his precious box, holding the pursuers at bay with a revolver. As he was about to disappear in the fog, a policeman patrolling the Seine embankment grabbed him. Prado shot him in the face, but the policeman hung on. This alerted a flock of agents on the quay who seized the thief and his stolen coffer. Until this moment the wounded policeman's street combat had amounted to shooting rabid dogs. Later he received a medal for apprehending not a mere thief, but one of the most dangerous criminals in Europe.

At first nobody connected the so-called Count de Linska de Castillón, arrested for attempted murder and robbery in Paris, who for two years in hiding had engineered over 400 other heists in the Midi, with the violent death of Marie Aguétant. Lorenzo, the jewel merchant, had mysteriously disappeared. It seemed Prado would go free since there was no one to accuse him.

But when Eugénie was nabbed for theft with several women soon after the police captured her lover, she tried to reduce her sentence by spilling everything she knew about him, including the dead whore. Prado never thought betrayal would come from someone so low.

Ordinarily, the police wouldn't have believed her. But Prado didn't realize that while he was in hiding, Monsieur Guillot, examining magistrate on the Aguétant case, had been piling up evidence against the flamboyant foreigner who had escorted Marie at the Eden Theater. Prado's sobbing mistress confirmed everything Guillot already knew.

* * *

At the trial the state called fifty-three witnesses. Prado's destitute wife made a melodrama of his brutality. "She was half-witted *before* she went mad!" Prado roared. Dozens of jewelers robbed in the south of France pointed to the thief. Prado became the outraged gentleman, treating the judge's questions like the ravings of an idiot.

"Did you have relations with Marie Aguétant?"

"It's possible," the prisoner smiled. "I don't remember all the women with whom I passed an hour or two. That doesn't mean I killed her. I wasn't the *only* one she saw!"

He also claimed never having gone to Madrid or to the jewelers in the Ciudad Rodrigo. "I've sold jewels from time to time. I didn't know these were Aguétant's. I found them on a train." The judge showed him the portrait of Count de Linska de Castillón he'd given to Purita. He turned white. The photograph placed him at the shop of the Madrid jewelers who still had Marie's necklace.

Prado never confessed. On 14 November 1888 a jury, outraged by his insolence and "enigmatic attitude," sentenced him to death for murdering a prostitute, attempted murder of a policeman, theft, and fraud.

The murderer's most important revelation after the trial concerned a matter over which he'd agonized: the use of his body. He'd read in the newspapers about the macabre game played at the Faculty of Medicine with the body of Pranzini, executed a few months earlier. On the day of his execution Prado told Marie-François Goron, the new Chief of Criminal Investigation: "Don't give me to students, let me die in peace. Really, it's my fondest wish."

Prado and his guards walked briskly into the prison yard. Wearing a thin shirt he was ordered to sit on the plank. He bent forward to have his head placed in the lunette. But Deibler, the country's celebrated minister of death, noticing he hadn't pushed the prisoner's neck in far enough, took a full forty seconds to readjust it. Voices from the crowd protested about the executioner's incredible delay. Then suddenly, the crash of the falling blade.

Prado's remains were placed in an executioner's wagon which sped to the new Ivry Cemetery, followed by the carriage of Goron. When a delegate from the medical school arrived to take the body, Goron insisted on a burial. The delegate protested. Surely the wishes of an executed criminal didn't matter now. But Goron prevailed. Prado was buried in a pine box along the cemetery's southern avenue, the first condemned man to lie there, the first in many years with the forethought to direct the fate of his corpse.

4 Headpiece

4 December 1891, 42 Boulevard du Temple,
XIth Arrondissement, Emilie Dellard, 75,
stabbed in her apartment by François-Louis
Anastay, 25, sub-lieutenant in the French
Army. Anastay also stabbed Dellard's maid,
Delphine Houbré, who survived.
Sentenced to death 26 February 1892.
Guillotined 9 April 1892.

Whatever constitutes my thinking being won't be destroyed immediately. I believe I'll survive around an hour. Come to my execution, Léon. Insist my head be delivered to you. Gaze on it, dear brother. At the sound of your voice, the eyes will respond. Be sure the doctors are present. Make them ask it questions. For "Yes," the eyes will turn right. For "No," they'll turn left.

The question of survival after death will be resolved, and I'll have advanced the cause of science. Let our father attend to the autopsy of my cadaver. He'll want my brain analyzed.

* * *

Life was intolerable in the regiment. I had a reputation for pleasure and big spending. My debts and all the time I spent in the casinos were considered unbecoming to an officer. My superiors weren't very intelligent, so I didn't bother finding subjects we could discuss. They decided I was quite ignorant on military issues. Mainly, they were jealous. So many women found me attractive. The keeper of my lodgings reproached me when I showed up with two ladies, one after the other. "Monsieur! One doesn't do *that!*"

Why? Love is all that matters. Who can resist those incredible beings who make us palpitate, sear us with ecstasy, and cause our imaginations to explode? I've let them direct my path. Right now women all over the world are praying for my release.

In Lyons I kept a little Spanish dancer, Madeleine Gonzales from the Bellecour Theater. I gave her 220 francs a month when my salary was only 225. Is that drastic? I think not. It's the kind of sacrifice we make when we put our feelings first. My corporal said living with a dancer disgraced the regiment and tried to make me leave Madeleine. I couldn't.

This didn't keep me from waltzing with Valérie Rey at the Casino des Charbonnières and proposing marriage on the spot. Her mother said to forget the idea. The girl didn't have a proper dowry. With my salary going to the dancer, I was also financially embarrassed. I asked Val to come and live with me in Paris where she could give piano lessons. She wrote: "Has that holy grail you're supposed to get arrived yet?" meaning my inheritance.

My debts forced me and Madeleine to live apart, which is how I took up with Valérie. I'd also fallen in love with Joséphine Gaçon. I looked her up in Paris to renew our relations, but her parents broke it off.

Father wouldn't give me the money I needed. You're the one he loves best, Léon! I read novels and dramas in the newspapers where people who take the right precautions kill and never get caught. I thought that with cold resolution I would succeed. Baroness Dellard was old and rich. We were well connected. Her son in the Ministry of War recommended me to military training at Saint-Cyr.

Papa neglected me. The Dellards treated me like their own child. Madame Caboret, the baroness's maid, was the mother of a school friend. She told me her mistress stayed at home and kept large sums of money in a secretary. At a bazaar I bought a knife to stab with, and another as a back up for cutting.

* * *

I wore my dark blue overcoat with diagonal stripes, alternating matt and shiny. I'd pawned it but got it back for the occasion. I crowned my head with a silk top hat. I'm not a common criminal. I lunched with the Chevret girls on the Rue Amélot to be in the neighborhood. Besides, I needed a full stomach for my afternoon program.

I went to the Boulevard de Filles-de-Calvaire. But the baroness had moved. I wheedled her new address from the concierge. It wasn't far away. I ran to the Boulevard du Temple, climbed to the second floor on the court, and rang the bell. Imagine my surprise when Baroness Dellard herself received me.

"It's you, Louis! What good wind brought you here?"

"I've come to pay my respects."

"Enter, dear child. Tell me of your last trip. How's your career progressing? You can only rise to higher and greater honors." That's what she thought. Her father had been a general. Her brother was an officer. Her late husband, also an officer, was the son of Jean-Pierre Dellard. His acts of bravery during the Revolution and Empire were the kind you read about in novels.

"Are you alone, Madame?"

"Yes. Not really, my maid's gone out, but she'll soon return."

"Madame Caboret?"

"Our friend got too old. I've a young maid now."

"May I see your son's room? He's been so good to me." I'd taken the big knife from my overcoat. She was leaning against her son's bed. I noticed a portrait on the wall and pointed toward its stern countenance. "Isn't that your husband?"

"Yes," she said, tilting her head toward the effigy. "Doesn't his son resemble him?" Her neck was practically against my face. I grabbed her and raised my weapon. Her look of supplication was terrible. I struck her on the chin with all my strength. My next blow to her throat was fatal.

She fell. Blood was everywhere. Her husband stared at me from his frame. To escape him, I ran to her room and broke open an armoire. Only a jewel box with military decorations. I returned to her red gullet. I didn't let its grimace divert me. I pulled off a glove to search her skirts. Her keys opened a desk. Nothing but papers. Still grasping my blade I ran to the dining room and opened a cupboard. Bonds, money and jewels. I was about to take them but stopped. A door opened from the service stairs.

"What do you want?" The maid had a nasty mouth.

"What I want . . . !" I lunged and started "sawing." At the trial she said I was "sawing her neck." I dropped my weapon and tried to reach my other knife but couldn't find it and still restrain her. Her resistance was fierce, Léon. I grabbed my hat and umbrella, and ran.

It was already dark. I sailed toward the main gate, but the maid was at the window. Her head swung like a lantern. Her screams were flames. "Help! Stop the assassin! There's the unmanly coward! He killed my dear mistress!"

Years of military training served me well. I was in full control, a man of the world, a family friend of the Dellards. I could only wonder what possessed the demented girl. "Shut the door," I warned the dull concierge. "He's still inside. Don't let him out! If an assassin's loose in the house, we'll lock him up until the police arrive." I left. I had to hurry. Madame Abbée-Delondres and her son were expecting me for dinner on the Boulevard Beaumarchais.

I forgot my big knife in the apartment and my glove. I was sorry to lose such a fine accoutrement but decided the fates, having foiled me in this escapade, would at least grant me another glove. I threw the little knife in a sewer on the Rue de Crussol. I ducked into a public toilet in front of the Cirque d'Hiver where I changed my soiled cuffs for new ones and washed the blood from my overcoat and trousers.

*Chambre de la Baronne Dellard où s'est déroulé le drame
(On voit sur le parquet près du lit les maculatures)*

ROOM OF BARONESS DELLARD WHERE THE DRAMA UNFOLDED

(One sees the stains on the floor near the bed)

Dinner was enchanting. Pâté Tivolier, filet de bœuf with Péri-gord truffles, a '78 Bordeaux Rieussec, in my honor, and a charlotte russe! My head didn't betray the least preoccupation. Optimism always returns with a good Bordeaux. The Abbée-Delondres urged me to dine with them the next day, which I did.

News of my crime was all over Paris. "Did you know your pro-tector's mother Baroness Dellard has been murdered?" Madame Abbeé-Delondres asked.

"Yes," said I with perfect aplomb. "Apparently a young girl flew out a window." My hostess didn't find my response offensive, so I ventured a question about her financial situation.

"My dead husband's pension still isn't liquidated. I never keep more than 100 francs in the house. Thieves are everywhere!" She laughed. Was she reading my mind?

Of course, Madame Dellard's son was devastated about his mother, as I'd have been. He has a shrewd head and did his own investigating. When Madame Caboret, the former maid, mentioned my name he had a flash of recognition. Maybe he knew about my financial difficulties and told the police.

I hadn't fled Paris. I had a quiet room overlooking the Palais Royal. I was reading, enjoying the city, and loathed the idea of de-parting. It took them three weeks to find me. By then my beard had a fierce growth. I shaved it off to restore my profile to its characteristic distinction before the camera of Monsieur Bertillon.

Bertillon. When that death's head photographed me at the Pre-fecture I moved and had to repeat the performance.

"That's six more sous you're costing the government."

"Poohy!" said I. "You gentlemen have always got the secret funds!" This incident was noted as further evidence of my reputation as an *épateur,* a shocker. What can you do with bores like Bertillon but make small talk to clear the lugubrious atmosphere they create? How could someone with his files and numbers, who haunts the dregs of humanity, understand a man of my sensibilities?

Confessing to Chief of Criminal Investigation Goron I found more merry company, again as the principal guest! I wept profusely, which raised a nagging thirst. I asked for Bordeaux, but Goron was so gracious in bringing me water I didn't object. I required several glasses to maintain my composure. Goron's an old soldier. I told him all about the Lebel rifle. The army would find it advantageous to look into this weapon. He looked at me as if I'd missed the point of our meeting.

Monsieur Gévelot, cousin of my victim's son, came to be with me during the interview. He was equally kind, soft spoken, not at all angry. How decent some people can be. "Yes, yes I'm guilty — miserable wretch that I am," I cried. "Ah, you people don't know what it is to murder someone." I'd have denied everything not to be accused of disgracing my uniform, but as I told Gévelot, "Our talks have touched me to the heart." Then I gave Goron my opinion about the epaulet and the Ministry of War's mistake in letting only officers wear this shoulder ornament.

* * *

They've had the nerve to put me in a cell with someone who raped his own daughter. I'm humoring this aberrant specimen by letting him teach me classic slang. But I can't concentrate with such brutes around. Report it to the press, Léon, so they'll tell the public.

Despite this impediment I've memorized some speeches from the plays of Corneille and Racine. The guards are impressed by my declamations. Why not? It's dismal for them, playing cards all the time. I'm also painting and writing verse. I gave Monsieur Goron "The Dance of Thoughts," a sonnet I can't get out of my head, a kind of ecstasy, which I hope expressed my appreciation. You know my poems so I won't quote it here. Do you like my letters in rhyme?

I'm on page eighty of my memoirs. Kind of a jumble, really a list of events which pays special attention to my childhood in Lyons. I've entitled them *The Genesis of a Crime*. The hero is named Georges, myself thinly veiled. I suppose I should put Georges in the German army so I won't be recognized, but how can I describe a locale where I've never lived?

* * *

At my trial weren't you pleased by the crowds who came to hear my story? How many people have my kind of courage? I greeted them with a military salute. No hard feelings. My destiny was in the hands of Henri Robert, a compassionate *avocat* who finds the death penalty useless and stupid. I knew I'd have to suffer certain indignities from his argument.

"Sub-Lieutenant Anastay was retired to non-active service because of poor vision. They locked him up for four days because he didn't salute the chief of the battalion. This was not effrontery. He couldn't recognize him! A military eye exam shows his visual problems notably affected his central nervous system. His crime is the result of a diseased brain. It's months since his arrest, and he still hasn't been seen by an alienist. For a fair trial we must have testimony from doctors who've examined him."

That's my defender. The judge's mustache moved and asked if I wanted to be examined. My eyes turned right. "Yes." But mysteriously, the mustache denied Robert's request.

So he brought in his own specialists. "Anastay shows atrophy of the optic nerve, symptomatic of a lesion in the central nervous system. Dr Charcot of the Salpêtrière has shown this precedes clear manifestations of nervous illness." Another doctor agreed. "There are intimate connections between the eye and the brain. Drs Charcot and Lambroso reinforce these views."

I felt good. Charcot and Lambroso are supposed to be experts on lunatics. Then we heard from Monsieur Cruppy, the prosecutor. "Anastay is very intelligent."

I was flattered.

"He chose his victim carefully and premeditated the crime."

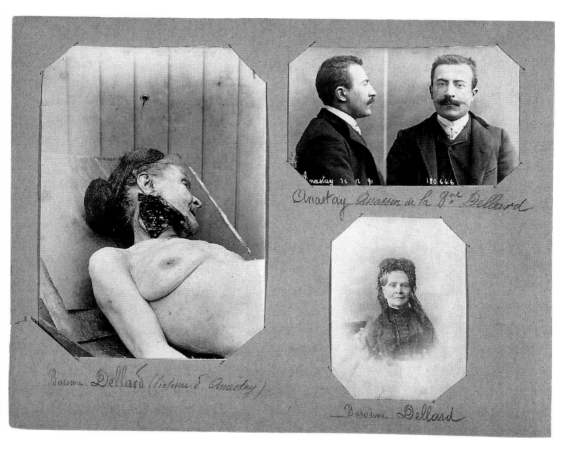

ANASTAY, MURDERER OF BARONESS DELLARD

Baroness Dellard (victim of Anastay)

Cruppy was dangerous. He used my brains against me. He also destroyed the case for my bad eyes.

"He saw well enough to slice the baroness's neck where it counted and do the same to the maid. He used the same eyes to flee without being seen. With this eye business, we're masking cold-blooded murder. The central nervous system is not necessarily the center of the brain. The cause of Anastay's weakness is his *doctors* whose testimonies are mere euphemisms. As for his position as an officer, the only military courage he's ever shown is killing an old lady! He even subscribed to a paper, published by a financial society, to study investments so he'd know what to do with her stolen fortune!"

Head, held high, I endured these treacheries.

"What about debauchery?" Cruppy cried. "That weakens the eyes." He pulled out a farewell letter I'd written Valérie a week after the crime and read it aloud.

Dearest Val,

The doctor I've consulted says my eyes are in a grave state. I have anemia of the retina, very difficult to cure. I've been advised to greatly moderate my pleasures, a remedy hardly calculated to amuse me. Adieu my *bébé*. I kiss your titties.

Ernest

I blanched at the last phrase, but Cruppy was triumphant. I was trying to let Valérie down easy, but he called the poor girl a tramp.

"There gentlemen, you have his eye malady and its origins."

One of the Mademoiselles Chevret, with whom I'd lunched before the crime, testified I was sweet and intelligent. I broke down sobbing, my head in my hands. My tears were sincere. As I've written, "We unfurl in the breath of love."

Delphine, the maid, confronted me with the confidence of a head restored to its shoulders. "Mind what you say, Madame. It's my head you're putting in peril." How different from Madeleine or Valérie or

Joséphine. If I'd been able to eliminate this Jack-in-the-Box no one would have recognized me. I'd have denied everything and been acquitted. "She's quite mistaken," I told the court. "It's an insult against an officer of the French army to suppose me capable of such a thing."

"When he was young he was very sweet. But he became lazy and didn't work." My hands flew to my ears. Those are the gaping mouths of Monsieur and Madame Caboret betraying me. Other so-called friends fueled the flame with similar abuses.

The judge made me repeat my confession: "An invincible force pushed me. Her head was in front of me. I raised my hand and hit. She fell in her own blood. I still can hear the rattle, more terrible than any pain I could inflict on myself. I accept responsibility for my flight and feel I should climb the scaffold." After that burst of dancing thoughts, what could Monsieur Robert do? True to his principles, he argued for life imprisonment. But the jury decided: "Off with his head!"

* * *

I'm still a soldier, Léon. But now I'm in the reserves, ready, when called, to serve the guillotine. If I haven't suicided it's because I believe in God, and God forbids us to take our own lives. I have long conversations with the chaplain. The words of this holy man console me. Sometimes we pray, *tête-à-tête*, in a glow of heavenly splendor. He told an inspector, "I'm sure Anastay will go straight to paradise. He has such a pure soul. God simply has strange and incomprehensible routes to lead him there." His sympathy is genuine, Léon. Don't you think?

When my appeal was rejected I stopped eating. Terrible nightmares poured from my head. The worst was the baroness's look of supplication. The chaplain tried to prepare me for my execution. It sounded dreary and frightening. I couldn't bear to think of my head swimming in space.

Wouldn't it be possible, Léon, to create a human being from a mass of inert matter? One could conceive of a worker sufficiently skilled at creating the seed of a plant, down to the last detail. This seed, absolutely the same as that which would have served as the model, will germinate into an infinitely superior being and bear the principle of life. I leave this to you. Please look into it. If you are able to create such a being, make it more perfect than man and give it a spirit which will permit it to interpret metaphysics better than we've been able to.

* * *

I hoped the experiments I'd requested would be performed. But no one called so I could answer. Why Léon? Why wasn't there an autopsy? Didn't father want to know what was wrong with me? A grave was prepared at Ivry. My head protested, turning left, "No!" But I was covered with dirt.

The next day Madeleine, my little Spanish dancer, placed a wreath of flowers on the site. The police removed her tribute. Placing flowers on the tombs of executed criminals is forbidden, even to one as extraordinary as your brother François-Louis Anastay. Why didn't you and father come? Do you still love me, Léon? Does father?

ARCHIVES DE POLICE, DOSSIER ANASTAY

Paris 9 April 1892

Monsieur Prefect of Police

I would like to ask you for the authorization to exhume the body of my son, Anastay, Louis, left at the Ivry Cemetery, in order to have it autopsied at the Laboratory of Pathological Anatomy for Nervous Diseases, Faculty of Medicine, and have it reburied at the Cemetery of Père Lachaise.

Yours sincerely,

L. Anastay
25 Passage Saulnier

5 Argument with a Friend

14–15 May 1895, 151 Rue de Grenelle,
VIIth Arrondissement, Benvenuto Balardini, 49,
coachman, beaten, strangled, and stabbed by
Louis-Antoine Mas, 27, packer of military
equipment. Sentenced to forced labor for life.

In 1894 Armand Cochefert became chief of criminal investigation. He was a big man with a mustache that gave him the look of a walrus. His enemies called him egregiously fat and sometimes claimed that he was happier at his desk than chasing after criminals. Reporters laughed at him for keeping hard-boiled eggs in his pockets, gobbling them a dozen at a time. Preferring humor and cunning to beating suspects for a confession he was also a talented amateur magician. On many occasions he dazzled pickpockets by sleight-of-hand, stealing their watches and wallets just to enjoy the shock as he dangled these possessions before their eyes. But in the spring of 1895 he wasn't dealing with pickpockets.

* * *

On the night of 14 May, Benvenuto Balardini ended his shift around eleven, parked his coupé at the company's depot and walked home. His neighbors, Mesdames Bon, Marpron, and Rollet, heard two men climbing the three flights to the coachman's attic cubicle, drinking and talking. Suddenly their conversation exploded. Cries more alarming than those of the Italian's usual nocturnal *fêtes* kept them from returning to their lonely dreams.

The two men were threatening to destroy each other, smashing furniture, pounding until the ladies thought the partitions would cave in. Protests of love, snarling into hoarse curses, growled through clenched teeth. Then everything turned inexplicably quiet. While the neighbors stiffened waiting for the next outburst, a dead weight fell to the floor. For a quarter of an hour they held their ears to dampen the sound of something furiously being beaten.

Later, someone left the coachman's room, struck two matches, and bumped the walls descending the stairs. The concierge heard a knock on the window of her box, automatically pulled the cord, and the visitor left. Mesdames Bon, Marpron, and Rollet passed the rest of the night wild-eyed, never daring leave their rooms to console each other until the concierge arrived with the morning letters. Still in their night gowns, they flew, squawking, into the hallway. Like a chorus on cue they began to cry: "We heard everything. We believe Balardini is dead!"

The concierge knocked on the coachman's door. No answer. She looked through the keyhole and saw chaos. Turning the knob and finding it double-locked she called Monsieur Pélardy, the police commissioner. He lumbered to the eaves, pushed past the swooning females, and forced his way into the tiny cubicle. He found a battlefield of wrecked furniture, broken glass, and blood all over the walls. The coachman, naked, on his knees, skull smashed, lay under the window. His face was a grimace of knife wounds. A rope dug into his neck.

* * *

When Cochefert and his sub-chief Octave Hamard arrived, they began by looking for signs of robbery. From a nail on the bedstead

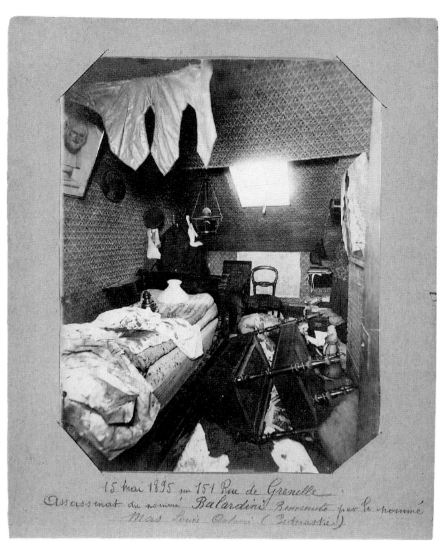

15 mai 1895, in 151 Rue de Grenelle
Assassinat du nommé Balardini Benvenuto par le nommé
Mas Louis Antoine (Pédérastie)

15 MAY 1895, 151 RUE DE GRENELLE

Murder of Balardini, Benvenuto by Mas, Louis-Antoine (Pederasty)

Cochefert retrieved a watch with a broken crystal and the hairs of the coachman on it. The hands of the watch, clotted with blood that had spurted across the room, were fixed at twelve thirty-five. Next to the body was a trunk containing the victim's savings of several hundred francs. The motive wasn't theft.

While agents searched the quarter and questioned the vagrants and prowlers which the May Invalides fair attracts around the booths, Cochefert and Hamard visited the morgue. Dr Vibert, the medical examiner, informed them that the coachman was not only strangled but suffered some thirty stab wounds. Whispering into his beard, he added that the body also showed signs of shameful sexual habits. The morgue ledger stated the cause of death with customary discretion: "Blows after an argument with a friend."

* * *

Alphonse Bertillon recorded the scene of the crime with his camera. Cochefert returned for another look around. Balardini's room, site of a massacre, didn't look like a pervert's, much less like that of a brutish coachman stinking of the stables. Actually, Balardini was a special kind of coachman who drove a hired wedding carriage for the Compagnie des Petites Voitures located on the same street as his lodgings.

To Cochefert the cramped quarters suggested a butler or down-at-heel dandy. Bertillon's photograph showed its antiquated gentility in the scrolled sleigh bed, washstand with spooled legs, and two carved Louis Philippe-style chairs. Maybe the furniture was part of the house, not his at all. Cochefert wondered. Still the coachman had enhanced it with certain novelties, seemingly those of a modest student of literature, even though the place lacked books. How else to explain the photograph of an ancient philosophical bust looming over the bed?

There were extravagant touches. A huge chintz valence suspended from the ceiling seemed torn from a festival canopy or funeral cortège. A leather hat box on the bed was a nice touch. So was the display shelf on the back wall holding a portfolio of papers. A map of

Europe under the window suggested a world beyond Paris. Balardini was born in northern Italy, near Ravenna.

Cochefert discovered his own face reflected in a mirror on the wall. It wasn't the weary expression that shocked him. It was the wide length of lace surrounding his drooping mustache — lace which the coachman arranged to frame his handsome features into a cherished keepsake. Cochefert stared and rubbed his eyes. The effect was unsettling next to the mountain of virile attire piled on the clothes rack.

Cochefert found the rage that had turned a coachman into a mangled body bewildering. This crime wasn't a theatrical of male sluts, aristocrats exerting superior privilege. The detective tried to understand the passions of common men, working-class homosexuals who hide like rats in public toilets and cemeteries, sneak across courtyards, copulate in attics, and kill in a fury. This was a murder, like any other. But the secrets of these players remained to be discovered. Cochefert was fascinated.

* * *

Everyone in the rooming house on the Rue de Grenelle fought to tell the detective how Balardini offered hospitality to many men and boys he met by chance on the street. They described the parades of nameless visitors on the stairs to the attic. "Parties all night long," chirped Bon, Marpron, and Rollet. The ladies told Cochefert how they pulled their covers over their heads to muffle the snickers and raucous mimicry, the sounds of alcohol poured into glasses, visitors and host hurling abuse, falling on the walls, groaning with pleasure, landing clumsily on the bed.

Cochefert learned that Balardini had lived for several years with Monsieur and Madame Lefranc, wine and fruit sellers at 16 Rue Surcouf. Moving to the Rue de Grenelle, a few streets away, he still took meals with the couple. A frequent guest at their table was a sallow runt of twenty-seven, Louis-Antoine Mas, who packed military equipment on the Quai d'Orsay and kept a tiny room on their street.

The Lefrancs told the detective about games Balardini and Mas played which expressed pent-up feelings surpassing the ordinary affection of comrades, which vacillated from awkward tenderness to outbursts over staged jealousies. They didn't know the Italian and his puny lover concocted the dramas to intensify their passion, make it exciting, even dangerous. Over soup Balardini and Mas brutalized each other in petty squabbles. In private they enjoyed the exhilaration of manly rage by getting drunk, lying naked, caressing, striking each other, weeping, and heaping apologies.

* * *

Cochefert questioned Mas but got nowhere. An agent guarding him felt the suspect was ready to confess, but a surge of humanity, embarrassment perhaps, kept him from extracting Mas's secret, and he was released.

Mas went immediately to Madame Lefranc's. The murder was already news. "Wretch. Admit it. You killed him," she shouted. He paled and left. Fifteen minutes later a café waiter delivered to Madame Lefranc a note that Mas wrote: "You and everyone else suspect me of killing the Italian. I'm not strong enough to answer your questions. I'd rather die than be arrested. You'll see me in another world, dear Madame. I leave you all I possess."

In the envelope the lady found ten francs. At the Porte de Versailles the wretched lover threw himself under a moving cart loaded with dirt, letting the wheels crush his chest. Ribs broken and coughing blood, Mas hoped he'd perish. He was dismayed to be carried to the hospital to recover.

* * *

The chief detective and his assistant found a bloody shirt in Balardini's armoire. It was too small for the coachman. They showed it to a laundress from the quarter who knew Mas's three identical shirts perfectly and identified it as his. The detectives smiled. They hounded

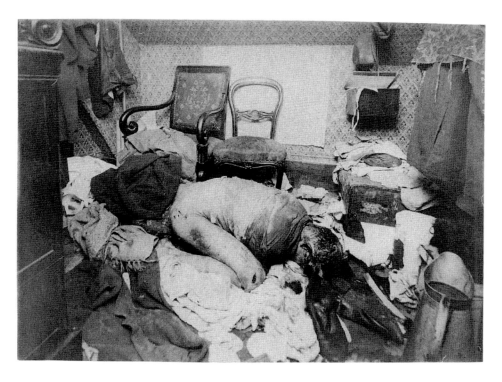

PHOTOGRAPH OF THE BALARDINI CASE FOUND IN THE ARCHIVES DE POLICE

(Possibly the image missing from a blank page in the album)

Mas in the hospital. Their dreary shadows overwhelmed the little man in the iron bed. Every day, for two weeks, they returned, staring at his pale face until he whined a confession and described the crime.

"Balardini and I ate with Monsieur and Madame Lefranc, as usual. The Italian stroked his mustache and started flirting with the lady, knowing it would enrage me. Truth is, I was courting her. But she was taken with the coachman. Don't think he didn't enjoy reddening her cheeks. She wouldn't even consider my attentions.

"In his room we drank some rum and started fighting. That's when I decided to torment him with my little secret. That I'd had sexual relations with her. 'Have you noticed how you've upset her husband? He's going to forbid us both to come to the house.' Balardini was the jealous one. He thought he was a god, a force of nature.

"I'd always been afraid of him. He was big and brutal. He said I wouldn't leave his room alive. That's when I hit him with a bottle. The blood made me blind. I grabbed a hammer, chairs, pieces of broken glass, anything I could find, and started pounding him. I couldn't stop. It was a real butchery. Balardini was in agony, moaning so loud I was afraid of the neighbors. To shut him up I put a rope around his neck and pulled it with all my strength. I had my foot against his head."

Cochefert mentioned that the physician who performed the autopsy on the coachman found evidence of relations of a special nature between the two men.

"Intimacy between us? *Odious practices*? Never. We were comrades. We were fighting over a woman! You don't know how many times he threatened to kill me. I was afraid. I hated him. I killed him in a rage. Now that I know he's dead, I'm upset. I miss him." Mas looked through the detective, flushing with shame.

To Cochefert, Balardini and Mas's life together was a theater of confusion, made plain to him by a detail in the murderer's confession. It corresponded to an explicable piece of evidence in Bertillon's photograph of the room.

The detective had noticed an oil lamp hanging from a chain above the sleigh bed. Bertillon clearly recorded its opaline shade, glass chimney, and metal body lying on the bloody mattress. But Cochefert hadn't known what to make of the dismembered object. According to the doctor, the victim sustained no burns. The lamp was used for something else.

Mas told Cochefert that after killing his comrade he noticed cuts all over his arms. Seeing the lamp overhead, he removed the shade and chimney and used the flaming wick to cauterize his injuries. He put cigarette papers on the bloody clots to form scabs, which he rubbed with dirt from the floor. "I did this to season my *bobos,*" Mas said with a child's expression, "so they'd look like old wounds."

Mas burning himself reminded Cochefert of older forms of self-punishment. A former soldier wounded and captured in the war against the Prussians in 1870, he thought of the way ancient warriors cleansed their battle wounds with iron tongs steaming from sacred fires. He caught himself. The association of these heroes with Mas was absurd. This was Cochefert's problem as a policeman. He would always project onto his investigations notions that surpassed facts punishable by law.

The detective considered the enthusiasm with which Mesdames Bon, Marpron, and Rollet had described the sounds that penetrated their partitions. To hear them flap about their ordeal, they'd all but smelled the death of their enigmatic neighbor. But of Mas, seated on the sleigh bed, quietly searing his flesh under the watchful eye of the framed philosopher, oblivious to the bludgeoned body beside him, the ladies straining to hear, knew nothing. Of his melancholy and torment, the ladies of the attic on the Rue de Grenelle heard absolutely nothing.

6   Philately

14 May 1896, 194 Avenue de Versailles,
XVIth Arrondissement, Emile-Julien Delahaëf,
22, assistant brick maker and stamp collector,
murdered and robbed by Guillaume-Louis-
Joseph Aubert, 30, morphine addict, publicist,
novelist and his accomplice Marguérite Dubois,
26, former waitress. Aubert was sentenced
to forced labor for life. Dubois received three
years for receiving stolen goods and harboring
a criminal.

Aubert is leaning on a tree in the Champs Elysées. It's a warm May day, the air heavy and sweet with sap. The smell is nauseating. He tries not to faint. He wants to lie on the grass, but he's too anxious, confused by dissolving pictures.

Before leaving his apartment Aubert had stuck himself in the thigh with ten grams of morphine. The dose was shocking, but today it's a mere stop-gap. He wonders why he doesn't feel calmer. Glancing at the lacy patterns of new green, he feels his head rise like a balloon from his shoulders. With a sickly grimace he waves it farewell.

Nearby, stamp collectors in the Carré Marigny are conversing in coaxing tones, trading compliments, making deals. The hum of the market is a fever, a contagion, the most seductive sound on earth. To Aubert it's a bedlam. He hates these connoisseurs fussing over paper

squares. Their gestures, the language they use to puff up their dia-
logues, revolt him. He wonders why he doesn't have their joy. Their
confidence. Their concentration. The sound of glassine envelopes
grates like a saw. The turning album pages are a riot in his skull.

"I've a sixty kopeck blue."

"Who wants a Uruguay 1872?"

"Here's a Cape of Good Hope. Not expensive."

"I've a package of 1,500 for 25 centimes."

He puts his gloved hands to his ears. "Maniacs. You'll drive me
mad!"

Aubert finds comfort in Moussette, whom he's brought along on
a leather leash. "Daddy wouldn't buy me a bow-wow," he sings, idly
stroking her back. He's deeply attached to this little black cat. She's
pretty and sleek, a more intriguing flirt than his mistress. Aubert
thinks of Marguérite, who is a little dumpy with a baby's lisp. Moussette's the real stunner. A royal addition to his toilette.

Aubert is wearing a slim black frock coat, a vest of yellow-
and-white-striped silk, and a broken collar, the last word in high-
life tailoring. Moussette tugs on her lead, lunging at a sparrow. Like
a woman distracted by a shop window, Aubert muses. The bird flies
to safety, and she returns to caress his trousers, a coquette on velvet
toes.

Aubert is suffocating. He wishes he could sweat, but twelve years
on the needle, and his body has forgotten how. His perfect attire
doesn't conceal the fact that his arms and legs are dry sticks. The
desire between his thighs died long ago. His tongue is sandpaper. His
breath tastes like rotten teeth. Since he was eighteen, Aubert's been
injecting fifty grams of morphine a day.

With this kind of habit, he's quaking with worry. He's down to
a few hundred francs. He already bled dry his mother and brother. He
told Marguérite to ask her parents for a loan: "If you refuse, I'll be
forced to enter a house and dishonor our family," she wrote. "That'll
loosen their purse strings," he tells himself. Her threat is close to the

truth. Her parents, puzzling over her letter, wonder what kind of "house" she means.

Suddenly, the attack. Aubert should have felt the warning twinges, but he was distracted by his rage under the trees. A jolt of electricity throttles his mouth, jaw, neck, collapsing his face into a sneering mask. His eyes, colorless holes, twitch and blink. He panics, "I'm drowning, Moussette," clutching the blur at the end of the leash.

Aubert has suffered these spasms all his life. His family, pitying his Saint Vitus's dance, let him rule the household. But in the schoolyard his trembling gait and mechanical head were hilarious to his classmates.

"I say. Feed the starving giraffe. And that nose aquiver. There's a cat going to sneeze. Drunken bear. He can't keep his balance. Crackpot! You're a crackpot!"

"You're all liars!" Aubert howled, whining, prancing, biting his fists, fending off the children with kicks and punches. Returning home he brutalized the servants, pummeled his mother. They had to restrain him with ropes when he threw a stone which bloodied the head of his grandmother. The thought of that outburst should make him weep, but he can't. He's all dried up.

* * *

Aubert hides along a gravel path until the spasms subside. He pulls himself upright, adjusts his top hat, feels for the pin in his cravat. He's supposed to meet a prodigy stamp collector named Julien Delahaëf.

The kid's been bragging about two albums he wants to sell which come from the collections of Arthur Maury and Baron Heinrich von Stephan, highly esteemed in the world of philately. As if Aubert didn't know.

Aubert decided not to confront Delahaëf right away. For weeks he observed him at the tables. A show-off. Clever oaf in some brick-making business with his father. Let him act the lord, I know how to skin him.

He sends Delahaëf a telegram: "Meet me at the stamp market. Gaston Darnis." The name is one of many Aubert uses for business. He studies the sky, thinking of Delahaëf, and feels small.

"I'm used to money," he complains to Moussette. His family, proud people, are wine growers in the Médoc. He's eaten their fortune down to the last sou. When his father left a vineyard worth two million francs, he dissipated his share. He rifled his mother's cupboards when she stopped her loans. Then a fire consumed her house while she was sleeping and forced her to live with his brother. Aubert received a large part of the insurance, but the needle and drink got that too.

Aubert is exasperated. Nothing he's tried meets his expectations. After the army, he sold wine, then rum — his own label *Léon XIII,* door to door. He opened a student bar, but his back-room tippling depleted the stock. He bought wine on credit and sold it to a band of swindlers whom he cheated by disappearing when the creditors appeared. He gained nothing but debts and a police tail. For trying to embezzle a piano manufacturer he got two months in prison. "Whatever I do is fated to turn out wrong and my heart lies buried as if it were something dead," he murmurs quoting an obscure poet.

Aubert has other names. Castel-Doumerc is a favorite for literary enterprises. He advertised in the *Biarritz Gazette* as "Monsieur Louis Castel, Professor of French Literature and Geography." Giving lessons might be fun. In more personal notices, he offered heart and hand to "any young girl with 800,000 francs." Or promised "disinterested and protective love to a young rich woman with temperament," inserting some lines from Hugo as if they were his own. *Mysteries of the Bois-de-Boulogne,* his novel, still lies in a drawer. He's saved his entire correspondence of some 5,000 letters exchanged in various schemes. In six years Aubert and Marguérite have had thirty-eight different addresses.

* * *

"My projects always reflect my passions. Literature and geography led me to stamp collecting. I'm intelligent. I'll surely succeed with these engraved butterflies," he thinks. But morphine demands all his cash, in addition to which there's Marguérite's dressmaker, his tailor, and mounting tabs at the best bars and restaurants.

Stamps inspire Aubert with dreams of greatness. He sees himself with a butterfly net, chasing glorious rarities of pink, yellow, and black with azure letters; ovals from Brazil, triangles from the Cape of Good Hope; the one-franc orange of 1849; the two-cent pink British Guiana of 1856; the Hawaiian blue "Missionary;" the tiger's head from Afghanistan. He thinks jealously of the Berlin Museum getting the last two Mauritius "Post Offices;" of the rest, he calculates Monsieur de La Renotière has four, the British Museum three, de Rothschild two. How many other collectors are hiding such riches? How many possess collections of all the issues around the world?

Gazing at postage stamps with a glass, Aubert dissolves in geographical mirages. In his delirium, noble heads of foreign sovereigns and profiles of La République become Medusa heads. He marvels at the fine engraving of the Guatemala macaw on a fluted column or the Indian with a forest of hair poked with parrot feathers. Acropolises, sphinxes guarding pyramids, Chinese dragons, draped allegories with emblems, Indians, like characters from Châteaubriand, Kashmir stamps with Sanskrit letters, troops of elephants, a locomotive blowing smoke, a steamer on a tranquil sea—all storm his brain like hallucinations from the cinematographic theater.

Everything novel and original ever invented. How wonderful that we paste these fateful illusions on our letters and send them into thin air. Aubert imagines himself a stamp, sealed to the magic carpet of a letter, faithful courier on train or ship, hurtling to exotic destinations with words of love, diplomatic codes, or the saddest and most terrible news in the world.

* * *

Talking to Moussette, Aubert waits for Julien Delahaëf, thinking of fluttering paper squares. To live now. To live at last! If he doesn't make good on stamps, he doesn't know what he'll do.

Aubert lifts his hat in a feeble greeting. Delahaëf, flustered, tries to make a joke. "Ah. You've brought your cat. Will she be your second in our little contest? Why are you waiting here? You said to meet in the market, not off to the side. Forgive me, but I've been looking for you for an hour."

Aubert is stung by the finicky precision. "And the albums?"

"I never do business without my brother. I need 4,000 in cash for both collections."

Aubert struggles to make his head register. "You won't take a check? But we must examine the stamps first. Shall we go to a hotel and discuss it?"

"Private room? No need. The stamps are first class. Maury and von Stephan are outstanding provenances for this material. We must make another appointment since you haven't brought cash."

They decide to meet at the Hôtel du Rhin the next day. After waiting three hours Delahaëf and his brother leave. Aubert was trying to acquire a checkbook from his bank manager. A bad check, he thinks, we'll disappear with the treasure, and that cock of the walk will be reeling.

He sends another telegram. "Meet me at the Café des Négociants, Rue du Louvre. Bring the albums. Darnis."

Delahaëf arrives with his brother. Alas, the bodyguard. After lunch the three enthusiasts examine the stamps. Aubert, calmed by his syringe, is hypnotized. They *are* butterflies, he breathes, almost forgetting his scheme. Later he would remember this afternoon with the Delahaëf brothers as the ultimate voyage to the moon.

"You have a sale," he murmurs. "Here's my check."

"But monsieur. Cash." The brother nods.

Aubert is trembling. "Why not come by my apartment? Rue de Versailles. Don't trouble your brother. Come alone. Bring the albums. You'll get your cash."

* * *

"Take Moussette and visit your sister," Aubert tells Marguérite.

"Why, darling? I saw her yesterday." She asks, but she doesn't press. Besides, it's a beautiful day. She can show off her lace parasol.

Aubert's in his makeshift library, peering through the blinds. Delahaëf arrives with the albums in a leather case.

"As I promised," he says, smiling.

Aubert offers the check.

"Monsieur Darnis. I came as you asked. Alone and in good faith."

"You're insulting me with your mistrust. You're a provocateur, Delahaëf." Aubert is in the schoolyard, reviled and ridiculed.

Julien turns his back. Aubert picks up an axe-hammer, aims it squarely at the boy's right temple and strikes. He grabs the Bottin directory to cushion his fall. Shouldn't dirty the floor. Marguérite hates a mess. He puts Delahaëf's stamps in the drawer with his novel.

* * *

"A terrible accident while you were gone, darling. Young man, a creditor come to hunt us down. Actually, someone I did stamp business with. There was an argument. He seemed to doubt me. I was furious! But I mastered myself. He raised his hand. I had no choice but to hold my ground. I hit him. He fell. He's dead."

Marguérite listens, lips parted. "This is very unpleasant to come home to," she lisps. "It's your affair. I shan't have anything to do with it. I'm tired. I've my novel to read." She rubs her temples with witch hazel and goes to bed with *Louise de la Vallière*.

Aubert takes a cab to the stock exchange where he sends two notes to Delahaëf's father. "Don't worry. Sleeping in Varenne-Saint-

Hilaire." The second note is an afterthought: "Sold my collection for 10,000 francs. Gone to Chicago." He signs both "Julien."

* * *

Aubert studies a sturdy hat trunk his mother gave him years ago and lifts Delahaëf into it, folding the legs, arms, head, every which way. The gangly boy won't fit. He goes to the Bazaar de l'Hôtel de Ville and buys a bigger, deeper trunk. He needs something to absorb the blood. "Where can I find some sawdust?" he asks his concierge.

He struggles to remove the boy's trousers. The body is already stiff. We must prevent annoying evacuations, thinks the constipated morphinomaniac, stuffing a rag in the anus of his victim.

Next day Marguérite scrubs the floor of Aubert's library with potash, while he sells the Maury album for a measly 600 francs.

"*Chou-chou*! You're not to blame for this terrible accident!"

"I've never hurt anyone, not even a bird!" Aubert presents her with a ring and a silver bracelet.

Aubert discovers he has superhuman strength. He loads the trunk containing Delahaëf on his back and carries it downstairs to the street while Marguérite looks for a covered cab. They're amazed not to meet their neighbors or the concierge. They'd prepared a little story to explain their departure. As the coachman struggles with their load they cry, "Careful! It's our best china!"

* * *

In Aubert's library Delahaëf was a corpse. Inside the big, red trunk he's personal baggage, the shell of Aubert the tortoise. Given proper seals and stamps, this cargo must be dispatched. But where? It doesn't occur to him to abandon it in a street or empty lot. "We're a traveling party of four," he sighs, including Moussette. As for their destination, "To the Gare Montparnasse," he orders the driver. A porter helps them consign the trunk to the baggage room. Escape? It's the last thing on their minds. They're attached to Delahaëf. Next day they return, claim the trunk, load it in a hackney coach, and transport it to the Gare de Lyon. The day after, they reclaim it again and take it to the Gare Saint-Lazare. "He's starting to stink. We must send him."

Aubert is thinking of letters, butterflies, sailboats. "The ocean," he says distractedly. "We'll push him in at Cherbourg. He'll be carried to oblivion." But Cherbourg's an international port with customs officers. "We'll take him to Couville, last station before the port, and check him while we investigate the beaches."

* * *

Julien's father hasn't seen his eldest son in days. "He's a passionate stamp collector. Known to all Parisian philatelists," he tells the police. "I implore you to investigate." But no one does. Monsieur Delahaëf reads the two notes he received. Chicago? Preposterous. Besides, they're in a flamboyant hand that isn't anything like my boy's. He brings them to Chief of Criminal Investigation Cochefert. "There's a crime here, Monsieur."

"Young men disappear all the time." Cochefert studies the old man's close-cropped whiskers, thinking the brick manufacturer looks like a country justice of the peace. He's biding his time. No one's found a body even faintly resembling Julien Delahaëf.

* * *

At Couville, Aubert and Marguérite leave Delahaëf in the baggage room. They take a train to the beach and hire a coachman to guide them to the deep waters.

"Is it possible," Marguérite asks in her most adorable baby talk, "without passing through Cherbourg, to go to the little port of Becquet at the water's edge? We're inquiring for a friend who wants to make this charming journey on foot to recover his health."

"Shallow as a wading pool along here."

Marguérite tests the depth several times with her parasol. There's no way to launch our trunk here, she thinks. We'd have to carry it far into the sea. If we put it in a dingy we'll be noticed. "We'd best remove him, darling," she whispers to Aubert, "and continue our journey."

Aubert, collapsed on the sand, aimlessly caresses Moussette asleep in her basket. Staring at the horizon as if it were wallpaper, he's sailing to Chicago in a trunk stamped with every color in the rainbow.

* * *

The station master at Couville is bothered by an evil smell in his baggage room. He calls the police.

"We'll break it open. Could be dynamite!" They lift the lid and jump back. Delahaëf, bound with cord, badly decomposed, wearing shirt, vest, jacket, but conspicuously missing his trousers, rises from the constraining box, as if made of elastic. His mutilated head, caked with blood and sawdust, regards his liberators with a reproach. Then he falls in slow motion, landing seated in a corner of the trunk.

Gendarmes surround Aubert and Marguérite as they get off the train at Couville. "You're quite mistaken. I'm Georges Castel, a publicist from Biarritz. The trunk isn't mine. The label says plainly: 'Shipment of Monsieur Bernard to Monsieur Castel at the Couville station.' We're taking it for him to Villers-sur-Mer." The station-master squints at the gallant, his companion, and the cat. If I don't grab them here they'll disappear across the Atlantic.

The authorities make Aubert face his victim. "You've no proof we're connected to this ghastly cargo," cries the tic.

"On the ashes of my parents I swear I don't know this man," shrieks the lisp. The police grab Marguérite's howling basket. "You can't have Moussette. She's our dearest child!"

* * *

The couple are taken to Paris. Cochefert finds Delahaëf's trousers in their valise. There isn't a mark of blood on them. He's puzzled. Did the boy drop his pants before his death? "Were you hypnotized? Magnetized? Used as a lure, Mademoiselle?" Marguérite blushes with shame.

BODY OF DELAHAËF, KILLED BY THE DUBOIS GIRL AND HER LOVER

(Page from the album found in the Archives de Police)

"Aubert made me go to my sister's," she says pitifully. "I came home and read Dumas." Cochefert looks incredulous.

Aubert needs morphine. A closed left eye and slack jaw give him the air of calling someone. "I'm suffering. Please. Give me a shot. I've begged the prison director at Mazas. I beg you, Monsieur." It's more than Cochefert can bear. Miserable addict, archetype of archetypes, he says to himself.

"Don't blame Marguérite for this. I did it alone."

Marguérite writes to Cochefert from Saint-Lazare: "Must see you. Extremely urgent."

Now we'll learn how Delahaëf lost his trousers. "And what do you wish to say?"

"I implore you to have my own clothes sent to me. I won't wear what they give us in there. And have them change the diet. It's irritating my stomach." She stops. "Is Moussette getting her cream?"

"She's being cared for by the wife of the Cherbourg prison warden. She's getting scraps."

Marguérite wails.

Aubert in his cell is an inert mass, rubber head dangling, eyes closed. Occasional morphine injections keep him quiet, though it takes four guards to master his fits. He tells his life's story to Henri Robert, his defense attorney, whose impassioned arguments save him from the guillotine.

Everyone agreed it was morphine, not Aubert's lawyer, that spared him. Albert de Bataille, reporter for *Le Figaro* at the Assizes, found the trial a bore. Marguérite, resplendent in black, could only whimper seeing Moussette's basket included with her parasol and other pieces of evidence. Aubert, lost in childhood memories, bit his guards. Seventy witnesses added nothing to the obvious: a stupid stamp robbery and murder of a young philatelist by a morphine addict with a tic. "Nothing of mystery, passion, or adventure here," wrote the weary journalist.

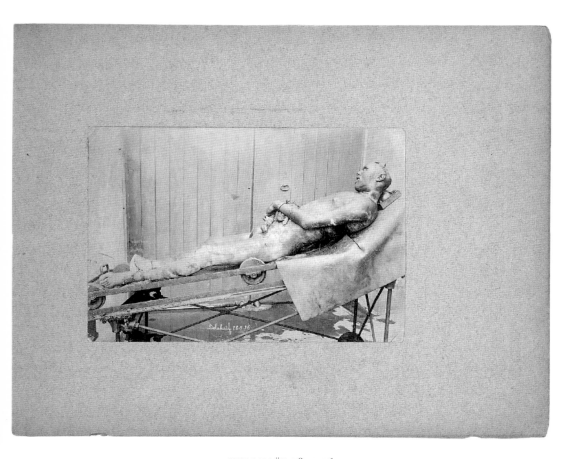

DELAHAËF 28. 5. 96

7 The Child Martyr

14 December 1896, Pierre-Albert Grégoire, 2 ½, living at 3 Rue Dessous-des-Berges, XIIIth Arrondissement, was discovered dying in an alley at 76 Rue Vaneau, VIIth Arrondissement. On 15 December he succumbed to bronchial pneumonia. For torture and neglect of his child Albert-Calixte Grégoire, 27, house painter, was sentenced to forced labor for life. Grégoire's mistress Françoise Deshayes, 37, and Widow Grégoire, 57, the child's paternal grandmother, each received five years of forced labor for complicity.

In mid-December 1896, freezing rain swept Paris. People in furnished rooms at 76 Rue Vaneau were troubled by sounds of crying but thought it was a cat, or the wind. A worker returned around eleven. The entry was dark. The gas had been shut off at ten. He tripped over a pile that moved and whimpered. A drunken woman, he thought. Fearing his kick had hurt her, he struck a match.

He saw a child, blond, about two. Head caked with blood. Right eye swollen. Oozing sores covered his body. The feet and hands were raw flesh. The rescuer called for the police. He roused his neighbors. They rejoiced that the child was still alive. A gendarme carried him under his cape to the station. Then to the hospital.

The foundling began to babble. He was delirious. He wouldn't eat. "Drink, papa," he cried, and swallowed some sugar water offered by the nurses.

Before dying the next morning, he sighed, "Papa ... mama." This told them only that he'd lived with his parents.

* * *

Cochefert comes to the morgue. Bertillon arrives with his camera.

"Show him naked," yells the chief detective. "All the sores and burns. Then dress him in the finery they put on before dumping him in the street. Get that too!" Bertillon shoots some pictures and waits, blowing his nose, while morgue attendants dress the corpse in the shirt, black petticoat, and sordid coverlet.

Bertillon's job is to capture an identity. But he can't. He's staggered by the battered baby. Needing to correct the facts, he turns the child's hands so the burns don't show. He hides the feet in the miserable drapery, arranging it in reverent folds, as if it were a holy raiment.

Cochefert has the pictures copied and circulated throughout Paris. Someone will recognize the child and report those responsible for torturing him and leaving him to die. But this will take time and Cochefert can't wait.

He orders the body removed from its refrigerated compartment. "Prop it on a chair in the morgue viewing room," he instructs the attendants. "The public should see him." Roped off from gaping spectators, it's a grisly display. The flesh is veined marble against the black cape. The blue eyes, half-open, have darkened to indigo. Anyone who knows him should address their letters directly to Cochefert's office at 36 Quai des Orfèvres.

Cases of odiously martyred children always draw huge crowds. Women will drop everything to travel from distant suburbs and join the lamentations. The bad weather should have kept them away, but 10,000 visitors appear. Gendarmes guide them past the occupant of the little throne. There are no outcries, only melancholy whispers and a steady flow of tears.

* * *

One visitor doesn't wait to write. She goes directly to Cochefert. She refuses to give her name, saying only that she's a nurse. She knows the child. For a brief period she had been hired to take care of him. He is Pierre-Albert Grégoire, two-and-a-half, son of Calixte Grégoire, a house painter, debaucher, and violent drunk, who lives on the Rue Dessous-des-Berges in the XIIIth Arrondissement with a coquette, Françoise Deshayes.

The child is not hers. Deshayes has three sons from other alliances. Six months ago Grégoire's wife, Auralie Lecuyer, weakened by her husband's neglect, died of consumption, leaving three infant boys, which he brought to the new ménage. One soon died of meningitis. Grégoire put another with public assistance, keeping Pierre, the eldest. Broken-hearted at the loss of his mother, the child fell ill and cried day and night.

The nurse's story eventually reaches the press. An anonymous reader, moved by the nurse's courage in coming forward, awards her 100 francs.

* * *

Cochefert is excited by the lead. He goes to the Rue Dessous-des-Berges on the southeast edge of the XIIIth. The houses are collapsing piles, widely separated by fallow vegetable gardens and empty lots strewn with garbage. Cochefert's carriage gets stuck in the mud. He leaves the driver and makes his way on foot.

He meets Deshayes' three boys who look anxiously at the looming policeman. Cochefert asks to be let inside. The apartment consists of a dining room, bedroom, and kitchen. How do six people fit in this shoe box, he wonders. Compared to the filthy neighborhood, the rooms are bright and cheerful, meticulously clean, and decorated with the taste of an imaginative designer. Françoise Deshayes has no such employment. She depends on Grégoire, and an elderly gentleman who appears from time to time, paying for her attentions with generous donations. She is small, with a red nose and coarse features.

"Did someone find Pierre?"

"He's dead, Madame."

"What? … It wasn't me. I had nothing to do with it. The kid's not mine. Talk to Grégoire." She tries to rub the flush from her cheeks.

Cochefert looks around for the scene of the crime. The flocked wallpaper and rosy velvet drapes seem an unlikely décor for torture. A large black poodle approaches. "Médor!" cry the children. "Pet him. He's very intelligent." Cochefert strokes the dog. He senses something unsavory, the smell of anguish. He holds the dog's head in his hands, studying the black muzzle. He gazes into the eyes of a faithful witness. "Confide in me, Médor. If only you could!"

Grégoire returns. Cochefert sees a bull of a man with thick brown hair, broad mustache, a grey overcoat and bowler hat.

"I'm here to take you to the police station to question you about Pierre."

* * *

It's midnight at the Quai des Orfèvres. Cochefert forgot to tell his wife he won't be home. He doesn't care if he eats or sleeps. He wants to scourge this couple. He grills them into the early hours of the morning, hoping to exhaust them. They're stimulated by the attention. They've done nothing wrong. He feels like a buffoon who's detained them for throwing a jar of conserves on the sidewalk.

"Don't think I didn't love my boy!" Grégoire reaches in his coat. "Look at him at five months, happy and healthy, right here in my pocket." Cochefert compares the photograph of the smiling infant to the grey swaddle in the morgue.

"But why did you torture him?"

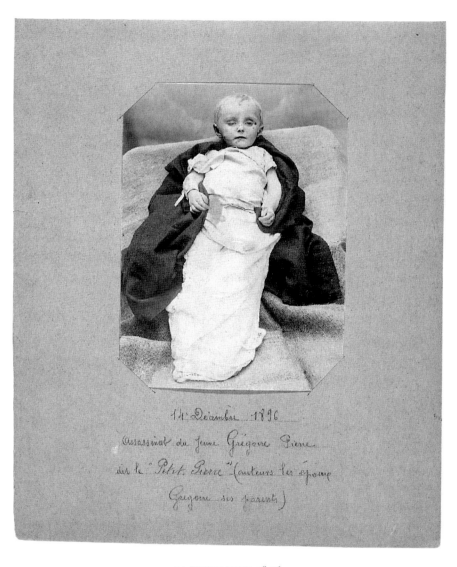

14 DECEMBER 1896

Murder of young Grégoire, Pierre, called "Petit Pierre"
(committed by the Grégoires, his parents)

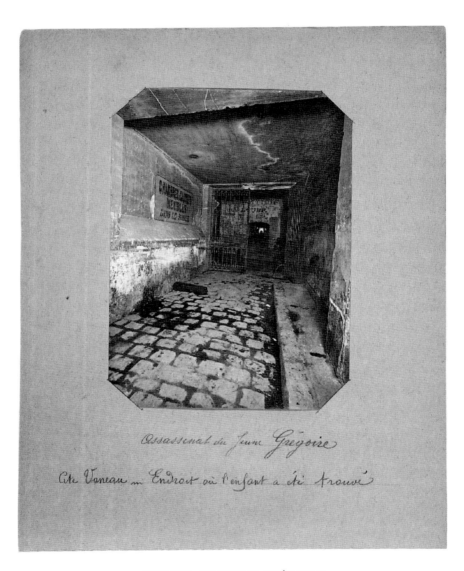

Assassinat du Jeune Grégoire

Cité Vaneau — Endroit où l'enfant a été trouvé

MURDER OF YOUNG GRÉGOIRE

Cité Vaneau, place where the child was found

Assassinat du jeune Grégoire
Autre vue de la Cité Vaneau

MURDER OF YOUNG GRÉGOIRE

Another view of the Cité Vaneau

"The kid crapped in his pants, made *pipi* on the covers. He stank. It was driving Françoise crazy. His mother passed on five months ago. Our whole marriage she vomited blood. Miserable wretch. I waited for her to die. She left me with three sick babies. Two got taken. Pierre acted disgusting. Françoise here's a clean woman. She gave us a home. Him carrying on, it's a wonder she didn't throw us both out. I live better than my neighbors now because Françoise is careful. I watch how I act with her."

The coquette glows at the compliment. "We didn't know what to do with this thing, horrible to everyone, moaning all the time. If he acted right, he'd have been well treated like my own. I raised them like gentlemen."

"He was a baby!" Cochefert's hair is standing on end.

"You think *you* know everything? *We* had to live with him! He cried. We couldn't sleep. I'm violent when I'm roused. I hit him. Few smacks to the head. He kept crying. Evil! Stubborn too! We had to nail heavy curtains on the windows so our neighbors wouldn't hear his bawling. A lot of fuss about nothing! Eh, Françoise?" Her face drains to a sickly pallor.

Cochefert strains to see through the bravado. Grégoire won't shut up.

"I love a smart dog. I put sugar cubes on Pierre's head so Médor would jump and grab them. He always knocked the kid down. It was comical. We burned Pierre's stinking cover. So he slept with Médor to keep warm. Those two dirty dogs kept each other company on a flea-bitten pillow.

"We had it up to here with Pierre. We stopped feeding him. What does he do? Eats the dog's food! Had a tough life, right? Who doesn't? I got stuck with three brats. Médor showed his teeth when I hit Pierre. The dog loved him better than me!"

* * *

Cochefert feigns calm. His questions only ignite their enthusiasm. He needs relief, to see them weeping, pleading for mercy. He brings them back to the apartment.

A mob of several thousand people, who learned the notorious address from the newspapers, are waiting to storm the carriages. They drag Deshayes into the road, beat her, and tear her skirts. "Scoundrels! Burn them!" Agents stuff her back into the vehicle. Seeing the scuffle, the driver of Grégoire's carriage takes a side street. Grégoire enters the house. His landlord steps up and smacks him in the face. "What a brute!" shrugs the insensible bully.

Inside, Cochefert, trying for tears, points to various instruments of torture.

"What's this fishing pole for?"

"To correct the little one when he wasn't good."

"And this?" He points at a Malacca walking stick with rattan fibers split into a harsh fringe. The head of nickeled iron still carries tangled blond hairs.

"For my strolls in the city."

"Also for beating your victim. Whose hairs are these?"

"Maybe they're his. I used it when he forgot himself—he crapped on my *foot*!"

Cochefert points to a large kitchen knife.

"I just tickled him with it. *Little* jabs, no worse than a needle! I stripped him to do this. Françoise doesn't like her linens full of holes."

Cochefert wants to cut their throats. He points to the stove.

"That wouldn't kill him. All right. I punched him. He fell. It was red hot. He got burned. I had an iron rod to knock him on the head. I heated it and burned his scalp and feet. I get worked up! The brat pushed me to the limit!

"He messed the dog's pillow. I put his nose in the shit to teach him a lesson. No response. So I put his hands in it. Then I put them on the stove. To dry them!"

"You held his hands there. You cooked them!"

"Sure! He wouldn't have done it himself!"

"Why didn't you take him, like your other son, to public assistance?"

"They'd see traces of my corrections on the kid and send the police commissioner. He'd look for evil intentions on my part. Don't believe the newspapers. *Oh, là là!* What a bunch of liars, these people who write! They say I abused him, made a martyr of him. He's dead. I say he died of natural causes. If parents can't correct their children, where are we?"

"You wanted to kill him!" Cochefert cried. "We've seen your father's will. He was highly respected. You were a drunk. You slept on the floor. He tagged you as useless and left his money to your kids. You got rid of them one by one."

"I loved them! I loved *Pierre!*"

Cochefert points to a hammer, used to crack the child's skull. Grégoire grunts and runs to the kitchen.

"See these?" He displays a pot of soaking linen. "Covered with blood. Proof the kid was a pig."

The mistress joins in. "They were so bad I had to put them in crystals first. I couldn't just wash them in one step. See? We took off his foul clothes. Put on clean ones before we gave him away!"

Grégoire waves for her to shut up. She stares at her shoes. Deshayes' children have told the detective she's black and blue. She never shows these "corrections" to the police.

"The day we decided to get rid of him, I'd hit him too hard. His eyes went white. Françoise didn't meddle. She knew what she'd risk! Besides, the kid wasn't hers! I saw he was on his last legs, so I took him to another part of the city. My mother was with us at the time. It was her idea to give him a fresh shirt and wrap him in her petticoat. She said there'd be no more noise, no public assistance after us. Get him out, and everything would be quiet.

"I wanted to throw him in the Seine, but Françoise, here, good mother that she is, said leave him near a dwelling. Someone'd take him in. We walked an hour in the rain to the VIIth where I'd painted houses. In the Rue Vaneau we put him in a covered alley, iron gates at each end. To keep him out of the wet!

"Françoise wanted to go right home, but I needed a drink after our hike. We went to a bar on the Boulevard Montparnasse for a few beers. Back at our place we sat smoking. Blessed silence! I said, 'Now we'll live in peace.' Françoise agreed, 'I won't worry now. My carpets'll always be clean.'"

Cochefert winces. He's supposed to fall for this perversion of bourgeois virtue? He wonders if he's dreaming.

"What then?"

"I broke the smelly dog's box and burned it in the stove. Françoise was expecting one of her protectors. We didn't want to lose his money. Everything had to look just right."

* * *

Cochefert puts the couple before the body and makes them explain every wound, the burned feet and hands, the bloody head. They speak of Pierre as if he were still alive, a stain on their life of ease. He brings in Grégoire's mother. She's tall, hard and, like her son who resembles her, carefully dressed.

"I had no part in this. I rarely went to my son's because of the irregularities there. I didn't want my daughter exposed to the kind of woman his mistress was. I lived with them a while. Then I moved in with my girl, a respectable dressmaker."

"On your rare visits, didn't you see how the child suffered?"

"I didn't really know him. I saw his head was a pulp. I thought it was healing from the heat of the stove. I couldn't go to the police. How could I denounce my son?" She puts her wrinkled hand on the child's body. The detective perks up at the display of feeling, wondering if it won't elicit some remorse.

"I gave my petticoat to wrap him. It's my son who did this. Why accuse me? I come from the provinces to face these annoyances! I don't want trouble with the police. Go ahead! Guillotine my son! I did nothing!"

"You're a woman, a mother. Why didn't you intervene?"

"Know why? This dirty kid never had the manners to greet me! He never once said, 'Bonjour Grandmaman!' He wasn't *my* son, sir."

"Isn't the child here your grandson?"

"I don't recognize him. It's not Pierre who's here."

"Where is he then?"

"I don't know. Ask his father."

Eugène Deshayes, the coquette's eldest, had fled the household terrified at what was going on. He's been taken in by his boss, a florist, who asks permission to raise him. This one, at least, will be safe, Cochefert thinks. He regrets having to send the other two to the dubious safety of public assistance. Before they leave he takes them into the hall.

"You won't see your stepfather anymore, or your mother, if you wish." The promise loosens a veil of pent-up sadness from the children, who for months watched a little boy burned and beaten, fearful they were next in line for the fatal treatment. They smile with relief.

* * *

Chief Prosecutor Atthalin is preparing for the trial. None of the usual defense lawyers wants to risk his reputation with Grégoire. The court appoints Monsieur Lagasse, famous for defending the anarchist Ravachol. Atthalin decides Bertillon's black-and-white photos aren't detailed enough to convince a jury of the horrors inflicted by the couple. He engages Monsieur Davy, an illustrator from the Faculty of Medicine, to paint eight watercolors of the nude child to use in the courtroom. The work will take weeks. Dr Socquet must wait until Davy finishes to perform the autopsy.

Newspapers begin publishing "martyrologies" of children murdered by their parents. "Kids living on the street are safer than these victims!" they cry. Other child beaters are reported across Paris. Shocked and helpless, longing for a collective expression of outrage, Parisians pester the authorities for the day of the funeral. But Davy's task of painting the child makes this uncertain.

During the long wait, impatience focuses on the morgue. The refrigerated compartments, designed to preserve the dead, begin to fill with flowers. Two huge, floral crosses arrive on Christmas Day. There are so many wreathes and bouquets the press implores readers to refrain until the ceremonies take place.

Packages addressed to "Petit Pierre" pour into the office of Monsieur Gaud, the morgue registrar. Under the wrappings, pinned to a sumptuous garment, he finds a piece of paper: "Use this to dress him for his casket." Gaud assembles a splendid mortuary layette: a white gown of tucked batiste, embroidered with silk thread and seed pearls; a white satin weskit edged in Valenciennes lace; a bonnet of crimped white tulle, cascading with silver ribbons; a tiny pair of pale blue silk stockings. A lace-trimmed sheet arrives to cover him. A white satin pillow and quilted coverlet come from a Russian princess, vacationing in Nice, who left her seaside strolls to commune with Pierre through thread and needle.

On the day of the funeral Madame Lecuyer, the child's maternal grandmother, dressed his autopsied cadaver in the gifts. She put the princess's pillow under his head and draped him with the lustrous sheet and quilt. She placed mother-of-pearl crosses on his breast and feet. In his finery, the baby lay in the little oak coffin, as if in a soft bed. Hundreds who viewed him at his grandmother's house on the Rue André-del-Sarte were consoled by the sight of an angel. He was safe at last.

On a frigid January day a crowd of twenty thousand followed the casket to the church of Saint-Pierre in Montmartre. Most were women with children taken out of school. All risked being crushed in the chaos of grief, but they were fearless. They'd joined a demonstration of unity they'd never felt before in their lives.

In the church, the coffin, raised on a catafalque, was piled with flowers. More on the floor rose to meet it in a mountain of white. Neighbors from the Rue Dessous-des-Berges sent a wreath of blue and white pearls. Grégoire's landlords also sent a wreath, as did police agents from the VIIth Arrondissement. The most impressive tribute came from Cochefert's agents, who passed round the hat at the Quai des Orfèvres for a colossal display of white lilacs.

A worker with a bouquet told reporters he had a dying child and sick wife who begged him to come. She said a visit to Petit Pierre would effect a cure and bring happiness to their family.

* * *

The offices of *Le Figaro* were flooded with donations begging Petit Pierre for indulgences. Two francs in postage stamps came from an "indignant mother" on behalf of her son Pierre-Maurice; a "mother of a family in Angers" sent twenty francs. Two francs came from Madeleine Granger, a little girl who asked the newspaper to start a subscription. Only children would be allowed to contribute. "Let us raise a monument to the little martyr who in Paradise will pray for all the subscribers."

Someone offered Pierre a plot near her family tomb. Madame Lecuyer had arranged to bury him next to his mother in the Saint-Ouen cemetery. She announced she would try to find his remaining brother in public assistance and raise him. But he had also died.

Cochefert received many letters asking to adopt Médor, a celebrity, a talisman everyone fought to possess. A journalist from *Le Temps* with the pen name of "Giant" finally got him. A gentleman from the Society for the Protection of Animals came to thank the detective for the solicitude he'd shown Médor. "At our next meeting I'll propose we have a special collar made to honor the brave dog."

It was rumored Médor would appear at the trial of Grégoire, his mother, and Françoise Deshayes. How testimony would be extracted from a poodle, even an intelligent one, was uncertain.

Médor was not the reason for the packed courtroom. The audience consisted entirely of women. Their compassion in providing clothes for the child and the energy with which they thronged to his funeral were not enough to satisfy them. They needed to see Grégoire, they filed into the Assizes to hear the fate of the murderers of Petit Pierre.

They were armed for combat. There was a profusion of feather boas. Even those of modest means floated to their seats in flowered frocks and boleros, waists of mauve satin, gloves of lemon-green. Women of higher station had dressmakers invent confections of champagne-pink or silver-grey silk, strewn with white polka dots, in the latest spring fashions. Their milliners built hats of green or violet straw, swathed in rainbows of tulle, garnished with ribbons and *éclats* of silk roses, camellias, and tulips. Since long white gloves were *de rigueur* for day wear, the women were buttoned to the elbow in classic kid.

Adjusting their lenses, they were also curious to study the person of Deshayes, perverted mother of three, destroyer of innocence through silence. At an appointed time during the questioning, a policeman paraded Davy's images through the courtroom. Two of them showed both sides of Pierre's body, blackened from his father's jabs with the knife. Another, actual size, of the head, hands, and feet, detailed burns where lost skin, which stuck to the stove, completely exposed raw flesh. The clear description and vivid tints were identical to plates in anatomy textbooks. By comparison, Bertillon's photographs were approximations.

Screams tore through the official silence. The women wept into handkerchiefs. Nauseated by the visual evidence and appalled by the shrieking females, who would have dismembered him on the spot, Grégoire slumped in his chair. "These drawings!" he sobbed to the bench. "They'll have me judged with too much haste!"

The lawyers for Deshayes and Madame Grégoire agreed: "This is the first time in a criminal case we've seen such liberties taken with the evidence. Bertillon's photographs are mechanical. Nature alone is reproduced, not some artist's interpretations."

"The illustrator is from the medical school, not any artist," responded the prosecution. Grégoire looked to see if anyone agreed. The jury wasn't listening. They were thinking of raw flesh, little hands and feet.

When Deshayes' defender described Grégoire's abuse of her and her sons, the women, momentarily taking her side, rose to applaud. Grégoire's sister, the "respectable dressmaker," not to be outdone, had an attack of nerves and was carried from the courtroom.

The sister of Pierre's deceased mother took the witness stand veiled in black, which stirred great emotion. "Grégoire kept me from seeing her. He neglected her and let her die."

"Put him to death!" roared the rainbow.

8   Two Waiters

6–7 February 1897, 4 Villa Michel-Ange,
XVIth Arrondissement, Antoine-Mathurin Pic,
17, waiter, stabbed to death and robbed by
Antoine Roubertout, 20, waiter. Sentenced
to forced labor for life.

Rohrer owns a café-restaurant in Auteuil. His waiters live in an attic dormitory nearby. Each pays him seventy francs a year for a cubicle with a fireplace, bed, chair, and tiny window. The rooms aren't exactly for living. They're holes to fall into after sixteen-hour days carrying trays and hoping for extras from the customers. Candles are used to prepare for bed. Water is from a hall spigot opposite the toilets. The passage is black when the waiters stumble upstairs. The only sound is a cat on the landing chewing mice.

Antoine-Mathurin Pic in cubicle number four was a country boy of sixteen when Rohrer took him on. He has no family in Paris, except a half-brother, Orluc, who delivers mineral water, and Madame Châteaux, a distant relative, who sells wine. Occasionally she serves him a meal. Since he always pays for this kindness, she finds him adorable. Pic's concierge is equally fond of the *petit garçon*. He is correct and steady. He saves his money. He never goes out at night, never sleeps away from his room. "Not a peep from that one."

Mathurin Pic's whole world is in his pockets. When he pays Madame Châteaux for dinner he shows her his savings. Once she saw a bank note and two twenty-franc pieces. When he visits his friend Alice Delapierre, a cook on the Rue de Cléry, he shows her his life-saver's medal, the bank note, and three gold pieces. He takes a coin and bites it. "Pure gold," he smiles. He's excited by the prospect of the Universal Exhibition in 1900. It's nearly four years away, but Pic has his ticket. He shows this to Alice. "Genuine." He's grave as a judge. She studies the ticket, running her thumb over the official stamp: *numéro 08.073, série 132.*

* * *

In December 1896 a young man in rags joined the waiters at the Brasserie La Fontaine. His name was Antoine Roubertout, a small braggart of twenty with a prominent jaw, clenched in a constant grimace. He had a mustache, hair in a brush cut, and affected a military walk. He had to borrow clothes and money from the other waiters to begin his job. Since he'd worked for a wine seller in Angoulême and waited tables in Rambouillet, Rohrer hired him as a *garçon omnibus* to do all the jobs in the café. Soon he became head waiter.

Roubertout liked going from place to place. Angoulême, Rambouillet, Paris. Nowhere for too long. He'd work harder than anyone else, gain top position and move on. He liked borrowing, using the rooms of the other waiters, sleeping with comrades in the narrow beds of their barracks. He stayed with Pic for several weeks before taking cubicle number three.

Pic and Roubertout came from the Corrèze region. To the younger boy, making friends meant flaunting his possessions. He showed Roubertout his savings, his ticket to the exhibition, and his precious life-saver's medal. Roubertout happily took Pic's clothes and loans of small sums.

Roubertout made fifty francs a month, which he spent as fast as he got it on rum and whores in Montmartre. Slightly tipsy, he'd walk through the café, looking for an argument. He told fantastic stories. Detaining a comrade in the kitchen, he'd say, "I pulled off brilliant feats of arms when I was in Madagascar." No one pressed him for details. He may have been head waiter, but the others didn't believe him capable of any courageous venture. He thought he looked the hero, but all the military decorations he wore on his jacket made the waiters laugh behind his back. "Someday I'll show you my knife. It's got a fine double-edged blade." The knife was actually the property of a veterinarian. When the doctor left it behind in the brasserie, Roubertout took it.

Pic didn't laugh at his friend. He loved soldiers' stories. He told his half-brother Orluc about Roubertout's escapades on the Indian Ocean. "Believe him, and you're a fool," Orluc told the boy. Pic didn't care what was true or not. The head waiter, with his noble jaw and glorious medals, was the most exciting person Pic had ever met.

On New Year's Day in 1897 Roubertout suddenly quit the café. "I feel cooped up. I don't get out enough." Luent became head waiter and took number three in the attic. "Why did he leave? Roubertout was *good,*" sighed Pic. He didn't understand why this migrant, always broke, had two other rooms, one around the corner, another across town near the central markets.

* * *

"You can't even pay for your dinner. If you're not working here anymore, I want the money you borrowed. And I want my clothes back," said one of the waiters at the Brasserie La Fontaine.

"I'm around the corner!" protested Roubertout.

"And if you decide to disappear?"

"Guaranteed, you'll have your money. Monday 8 February, the latest. I'm a man of honor."

On the night of 6–7 February 1897, a month after he quit the café, Roubertout, without a sou, climbed to the attic and pounded on Pic's door. It was nearly three on Sunday morning. "Pic! Open up! I've lost the key to my room. Let me bunk with you tonight. I'm drunk and tired. I can't wander in this cold."

The night visitor awakened the sleeper from a beautiful dream. Pic was at a fancy-dress ball, waltzing with Alice Delapierre, the cook. He was wearing his life-saver's medal. She was a princess in blue silk. He opened the door and fell back into bed, anxious to return to Alice and the ball.

Roubertout took off his shoes and lay wide awake beside Pic, waiting until he heard the boy snore. He reached for his knife, but it fell. Iron rang against the hard wooden floor.

"What's that? I'm tired and want to sleep." Pic pulled a pillow over his head.

The visitor now had a grip on his weapon. He jumped from the bed and threw himself on the dreamer. Suddenly, Pic wasn't dancing anymore. He was in the tropics of Madagascar, fending off an African insurgent in a fight to the death. He tore at the attacker, digging his fingernails into his neck, hands, and knees. But Roubertout had the blade. He raised it and slashed his friend's throat. Pic spurted blood. It flew onto Roubertout's shirt, soaked the bedclothes. Pic kept punching and scratching. Finally he let out a terrible wail—a whisper could be heard through the walls that separated the cubicles.

"Stop the racket!" yelled Luent from number three.

Roubertout was sitting on Pic, who thrashed and kicked in spasms.

The murderer swallowed hard, then answered brightly, "We're just fooling around, wrestling." But he couldn't stop. With sinister wit, he addressed his dead comrade, who was flooding the floor with blood.

"Come on, that's enough. He's right. We're waking everyone. Let's go to bed." Then the soldier raised his sword, and with a final blow, smashed the boy's skull.

The floor was a river of blood. It caked over Roubertout's bare feet. He pulled on his shoes. He took Pic's wallet which contained 150 francs and the ticket to the Universal Exhibition. Noticing some fresh shirts, delivered earlier by the laundress, he stripped off his bloody one, threw it over the body, and took a clean replacement. On this he pinned Pic's life-saver's medal.

* * *

Roubertout's concierge had pegged him as a braggart, but today she found his boasting absurd. Her son asked about the new medal he was wearing. The waiter took a deep breath. "I received this one under unusual circumstances. I not only rescued an English girl from drowning, I had the privilege of protecting the French flag."

The hero left and bought a new suit and shoes with Pic's hundred-franc bill. He wadded his bloody trousers and the stolen shirt in the corner of a cupboard. He wore Pic's blood like a second skin, hiding his filthy red feet in the new shoes. But blood from his own wounds stained his finery.

"And where are you going, looking like a duke?" asked a lodger passing him on the stairs.

"I'm off to the inauguration of the new extension of the Rue Réaumur," feigned the resourceful Roubertout. "The President of the Republic will be cutting the ribbon. I'll certainly get a glimpse of him." Roubertout wasn't going to any festivities. He went to the pawnshop of Madame Claudius where weeks earlier he had deposited a pearl ring. To get this back he traded her Pic's ticket to the Universal Exhibition.

Luent in number three was furious about the wrestling match that ruined his Sunday sleep. He'd half a mind to slap Pic's face. When he found his neighbor's door open and looked inside, his heart leapt. "Pic!" He ran for Rohrer, who called the police.

* * *

The press gave scant coverage to the murder of a lowly waiter in a suburban garret. The report in *Le Matin* showed noticeable disappointment. "During this period of calm, here's a crime that's a real windfall for the specialists. The assassin's bloody hand didn't descend miraculously from the sky. The police will soon discover his name, but this Sunday affair is pretty thin stuff. The victim is hardly more interesting than the murderer."

Chief detective Cochefert began interviewing Rohrer and his waiters. He noticed a boy hanging around and learned he was a former employee, named Roubertout. He was wearing a peculiar decoration. It looked like a life-saver's badge, but the virtues of such a medal didn't fit the boy's pinched face.

"Is that yours?" Cochefert adjusted his pince-nez. "Let's see it." Chilled by the detective's sudden scrutiny, Roubertout raised his arms to hide the decoration. As he did, Cochefert pointed to his bloody cuffs.

"I had a nosebleed Friday," explained the boy.

Cochefert was staring at scratches on Roubertout's throat and hands.

"You obviously have some information for us," Cochefert flattered politely. "May we visit your quarters?" Roubertout led the chief and an agent to a tiny room near the central markets. Cochefert ordered him to undress.

"Have you been in a fight? Your wounds are fresh. And what's this dried blood on your thighs?" Cochefert's assistant took the detective aside. He'd found a shirt with the same laundry mark Cochefert noticed on all the clothing at the scene of the crime, except for a bloody plaid shirt thrown on the body, which had a different mark. Cochefert sent his agent to find the laundress who did Roubertout's linen.

"I had his shirts. He had mine. We were friends, always borrowing from each other. I was working that night at the Montmartre Theater. Afterwards, a whore named Proserpine took me to her place. I forget the address." Police sergeant Midol, tracing Roubertout's movements on the night of the crime, discovered no one at the Montmartre Theater had ever heard of the former waiter or of a whore named Proserpine.

Cochefert had a doctor examine the wounds on Roubertout's legs and hands. "They're from fingernails." He asked the boy to blow his nose. The handkerchief showed no blood at all. The doctor discovered that Roubertout's feet, blackened with dried blood, conformed exactly to footprints in Pic's room.

* * *

Mathurin Pic's attic cell was too small for Bertillon to enter and have the distance to fit it onto the ground glass of his camera. Just as well, he thought, the battlefield isn't the room, it's the bed. Forced to shoot from the hallway, he had to drag the bed from the wall to get it in view. He'd have brought it closer to the threshold, but the fireplace mantel got in the way. He had to be satisfied with the bed at an angle.

Bertillon showed the battered boy swaddled in bloody sheets and blankets. One of his huge feet seemed to push against a bar of the bed frame. An eye, half-open and pulled to the side, gave his brown face an exotic cast. Lips parted, he looked like a fish gliding through linen waves.

The room smelled terrible. Bertillon opened the little window. Daylight mixed with the explosion of his magnesium flash. A cold February wind seared his nostrils, clarifying the odors of suffering and death. It almost seems as if the photographer wanted his picture to burrow under the waiter's skin, to penetrate the content of his dreaming.

The photograph was needed for the trial. Unless they saw the blood, the chaotic cell, the virtuous child sliced into a miserable corpse, how would these merchants, these pears, these cheeses, who knew nothing of real life, understand the evil rampant in Paris?

Years before, Bertillon had written about such pictures in a book on judicial photography. Like his measurements and portraits of criminals, these interiors were also his invention. They scientifically described the circumstances of a murder, the life of the victim. He recorded the interiors to drive the jury into a frenzy for revenge.

He didn't care if vindication meant due process. An eye for an eye was how he felt when he saw Pic's slaughter. Society would demand justice with *Lex talionis,* the "Lynch law."

Bertillon wanted to include the bloody hand prints on the wallpaper. But getting enough light on the boy meant sacrificing most of these marks to shadow. Other things in the picture accidently dramatized the story Bertillon wanted to tell. Among the bloody sheets were some shirts. The photographer didn't know the plaid one in the center was Roubertout's, stripped off and thrown over the body as he fled.

The flash, aimed at the victim's head, caught another shirt hanging on the bedstead. Its pristine whiteness, perfect emblem of the waiter's trade, contrasted with everything else in the room. Starch hardened its front and collar, stiff cuffs weighed down lightly rumpled sleeves. Perhaps Pic's laundress neglected to give the sleeves her complete attention, knowing they would be pushed up by a garter or hidden under a waistcoat. Perhaps Pic had already worn the shirt, and planning to wear it again, gave it a special place.

Pic's white shirt, miraculously unscathed, hovers in Bertillon's photograph like a flag of surrender, a sail guiding the boy's death ship. Its serene beauty recalls the spirit of its owner, believer in military glory and in cooks who become princesses; hoarder of pocket treasures — a ticket to a future exhibition to dream about, a badge for saving someone from drowning. By contrast, Roubertout's plaid shirt is a contortion of depravity. Although he didn't know enough about the case to attribute meaning to the shirts Bertillon counted on such things to speak through his photographs. Together in this picture, the shirts, a contest of opposites, are the eye of the tragedy.

* * *

Cochefert liked bringing a murderer before his victim. The technique usually led to a confession, which was a lot easier than roughing up a kid so he'd confirm what the police already knew. Facing the body of

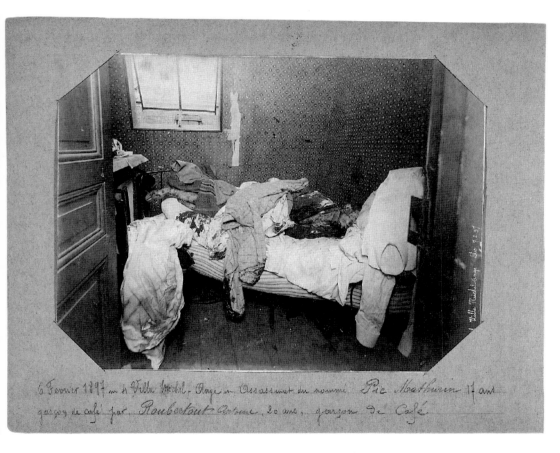

Murder of Pic, Mathurin, 17, waiter, by Roubertout, Antoine, 20, waiter

Pic, Roubertout emphatically denied any part in the crime. Such skill at concealment seemed to constitute a career. But killing Pic was his first crime.

Bertillon liked digging for details. He located Roubertout's married sister in Bordeaux and four brothers. They might have explained what led the boy to kill his friend for trinkets and a few francs, but nobody at the prefecture bothered to pursue the matter.

Roubertout tried to hang himself in prison before the trial. It was practically a confession of guilt. "They punished me unjustly. They locked me in a dungeon!" The Assizes finally heard his case on a sweltering June day. The accused risked heatstroke by enveloping himself in a long, black pilgrim's cape. The costume dramatized his isolation, suggested remorse. He hoped it would protect him from the sentence of death.

"I didn't have to kill for money. I could borrow it." Pouts of disdain betrayed his mournful shroud. He directed his statements toward the back of the room where the audience sat. It was pointless to look there for sympathy. Hardly anyone attended the trial.

The magistrate showed the jury a plan of the waiters' dormitory. He asked them to approach and examine the clothing from Pic's room. The men glanced at the bloody pile but wouldn't come closer. The magistrate showed the jury Bertillon's photographs, at which they also glanced politely. Their revulsion was clear.

Roubertout's battle with Pic was his first offense. His sentence took him to a penal colony, his first and last journey to exotic lands.

9 Belles Lettres

28 November 1897, 3 Rue Pierre-le-Grand,
VIIIth Arrondissement, Marie-Joséphine Bigot,
37, prostitute, found shot in the head.
Pierre-Marie Rodot, 42, former police agent,
arrested as a suspect and released.
Insufficient evidence.

My dear Sir,

What a pleasure to receive your kind enquiry. Let me immediately set your mind at ease. I'm on a tiny street near the Russian church. My beautiful building houses the Siamese Consulate. I mention this to indicate the quality of the neighborhood. But you mustn't be afraid that its distinction will in any way call attention to your person. Discretion counts above all else with me. My rooms are on the ground floor, at the end of a long corridor. The concierge knows to let visitors carrying my card pass without questions or comment.

As for the other concerns you expressed. I'm a woman of sensitivity with a Breton's warm heart. How I sympathize with your difficulties! What a burden to carry on one's affairs, support a household, and educate one's children. Such is the plague of our modern existence. No one thinks of the toll these responsibilities take on the man of the family.

Sometimes he has to break his routine and allow himself a moment or two to indulge his fantasies. We all want to surrender, even be a bit naughty, from time to time, especially when such pleasures are offered by a friend, in the perfect safety of inscrutable privacy. Ease and novelty are my specialties. I'm ever confident that you'll delight in the refinements of my experience.

Sincerely,
Mme Bigot

The letter is a response to "Timid in the Auvergne." As the writer sips her morning coffee, she addresses the envelope to a *poste restante*.

* * *

Joséphine Bigot arrived in Paris at seventeen with a teaching certificate. She became a governess but was soon fired for what her employers called "too independent a spirit." She worked as a maid but hated the abuse, false accusations for stealing, the kitchen scraps she was given to eat. After a few romantic intrigues, she entered a world more to her liking:

Gentlemen of finer instincts, I have curiosities to show you. Write if you're interested. Mme Bigot.

The classified advertisement was clear enough to those who knew how to read it. She also went to dance halls, theaters, and bars in Montmartre and the Point d'Elysées, handing out postcards on which she'd written a similar message with her name and address.

Responses to these solicitations, at least a dozen a day, arrived in the four deliveries of Paris mail. She answered each in a feminine hand, with felicities of expression learned in the convent.

None of the writers gave a real name. They signed in codes: "Monsieur 777," "Monsieur 69," "A Gentleman," or more poignantly, "Timid." She scrutinized their penmanship with the eye of an expert. Leaving content aside, she turned the letters upside down to study the flow of the script. She used a magnifying glass to examine the formation of letters, awkward hesitations, breaks in a word. She pondered poor spelling and punctuation, noted missing accent marks. Such failures were a warning. Her survivor's instinct decided if the writer were an ambassador, grocer, or sadist. Anyone performing poorly on paper got his letter pitched into the fire.

Joséphine Bigot trusted her shrewdness, her ability to read between the lines. If she found a sensual flow in the connections of the letters of the alphabet, she altered her tone from that of a coaxing mama to something bolder:

Dear Sir,

You can't fool me. In your writing I see the ardor of a sensualist. I'm excited to meet you. Obviously, you're a man who feels as I do, someone who enjoys the best that life has to offer. It's time you came to Paris for an afternoon of wine and pleasurable conversation. Who knows what affinities we might discover? Body and soul are like flames aspiring to greater intensities. I'm a musical creature. My body is a well-tuned instrument, ready to respond to all the subtleties of passion. We have much to share.

Sincerely,
Joséphine Bigot

She promised "love bites with my pink mouth and little white teeth," in candlelight or the glow of her fireplace. Everything in her letters, reassuring or gently seductive, was intriguing. Her concierge noticed her clients were rarely young. Most were older gentlemen, elegantly dressed. Some wore medals.

* * *

In a coquettishly furnished apartment on the Rue de l'Arc-de-Triomphe, a few streets from Joséphine Bigot, Pierre Rodot is at his desk writing:

Gentleman of forty in a comfortable situation desires a relation-
ship with a rich, unattached woman of any age. Apply to ... "R."

Rodot is the factotum of the Marquise de Marmoury d'Eclot. A rich
seventy-two-year-old, she is also a writer and collaborated for a time
on the newspaper *Le Succès*. She owns the apartment where Rodot has
a room. Madly dependent on her confidant, she refers to him as "my
nephew." He explains the piles of letters he receives daily as a necessary part of the secretarial duties for a low-level matrimonial service
under his directorship.

Sometimes he changes the text of his ads, offering to "come to
the aid of any young woman momentarily in trouble." He sighs at the
responses, endless portraits of women drowning:

Monsieur R., how desolate I've been since I arrived in Paris.
You've come along just in time. You *are* an angel of mercy!

Dear R., Since the untimely death of my husband, I've been
submerged in a tenebrous pit of grief, longing for a soul mate.
Until I saw your advertisement, I thought no one cared if I lived
or died!

Rodot's ads generate a huge response. His correspondence occupies
most of the day. He collects and organizes the letters in an archive of
cardboard boxes, which he keeps under lock and key. Most of the time
he finds the means to extract money from the all too willing damsels.
Or he'll take a piece of their jewelry and come to their aid by selling
it off, depositing the funds in his own account. Plenty of letters come
from women furiously demanding their money: "You promised to
marry me, monsieur!" Arrested for some of these intrigues, he's already in Bertillon's archives.

Rodot is interesting to the police, not only as a petty swindler.
Fourteen years ago, when Gustave Macé was chief of criminal investigation, Rodot was part of a special brigade of detectives assigned
to the Elysées Palace to protect the President of the Republic. When

the whore Marie Jouin was murdered in 1883, he watched Macé's fruitless investigation with interest. He and a friend, Franger, concocted a hoax and wrote Macé anonymous letters correcting details of the crime: "She wasn't killed with a hammer. It was a mallet." To lend more credibility to their observations, Rodot anonymously confessed to the murder. Macé, suspicious of the boastful ravings, threw the letters into a file.

Now Rodot, having made himself indispensable to the old marquise, amuses himself as he waits to inherit her fortune. Apart from maintaining and cataloguing his correspondence, he keeps other kinds of records. He's fascinated by the number of unsolved murders of some dozen prostitutes. Their names are regularly listed in the press to shame the police. He has an enormous clipping file with a dossier on each of these murdered women, whose killers are reportedly at large. He's underlined certain passages of newspaper articles on them in red. He also keeps notebooks with the names and addresses of living prostitutes who circulate in the more affluent quarters. He has certainly made use of their services. His notebooks contain drawings of the floor plans of their apartments, placement of the rooms, and the locations of their concierges.

* * *

Joséphine Bigot regards prostitution as good business. Her apartment with its foyer, kitchen, dining room, bedroom, and large bathroom, is not antiquated or bohemian. Strictly bourgeois, the rooms are reassuring to her gentlemen, as they are essential to her self-respect and well-being. On a whim she acquired some modern chairs in the *art nouveau* style, but the rest is a model of traditional correctness. The mahogany bed has a dark red serge coverlet. Eighteenth-century engravings decorate the walls. Chinese fans give the mantel an air of fantasy, as do small photographs of nudes in black stockings, which coyly suggest the pleasures promised by her letters. But nothing about them or the way they are arranged jars the effect of absolute sobriety.

Joséphine keeps her appointments in a notebook, which doubles as a record of her accounts. Twenty years of careful management have gained her a certain financial ease. She has good jewels, numerous stock investments, and property in the provinces. A woman of calculated risks, she's not above games of chance. She pays bookmakers at the race track to bet for her, always converting the winnings into more durable holdings.

Her letters, a form of personal expression reflecting her education, betray a profound loneliness. Like the women writing endlessly to Rodot, Joséphine Bigot longs for human contact. Written correspondence, with its respectful distance and pleasant suspense, until the final meeting in person, satisfies her sense of discretion. The men themselves, naked in her rooms, are a necessary, even rude anticlimax. She's forgotten most of these visitors but keeps their letters in two suitcases with her souvenirs — menus, gloves, and pieces of ribbon.

Writing also solves a practical problem. When Joséphine Bigot decided to make prostitution a career, she loosened her thick brown hair and undressed before her mirror to appraise the goods she was about to sell. What she saw was an enormous frame, sagging belly, heavy arms, jowly cheeks, and a coarse mouth. The creature in the reflection looked startlingly *homasse,* more man than woman.

When the gentlemen arrived and found their feminine correspondent quite unlike the seductress they'd imagined from her letters, she hoped their curiosity would make them stay. Like a bearded lady, she flaunted the obvious with an art of contrasts, draping her broad shoulders in a red peignoir, wearing a black lace shift, black stockings, and red slippers. The effect had a strange allure. The visitors discovered the "curiosities" she advertised were none other than the glaring facts of herself. She gave her clients vigorous sex. As they embraced her hairy bulk they felt they were fucking all of France. She wrote down the regulars in her notebook.

Her freakishness was not all that kept them returning. They were touched by her kindness and her laugh, which was that of a singer.

MURDER OF MARIE BIGOT, 3 RUE PIERRE-LE-GRAND, 28. 11. 97

Bedroom

After they left, she'd pull the protective covering off the piano she kept in the bathroom. Sitting at her instrument, as if in a proper salon, she'd play songs for the rest of the evening.

Her concierge, Madame Boron, was used to several days passing without seeing her, for Joséphine also traveled the country to meet her gentlemen. One of these was Monsieur Tremplier, a civil engineer in Argent. Eight years ago, he'd come as a client. He still visited her two or three times a month. Their intimacy was more than sexual. He knew how much money she had, down to the last five francs. He said that recently she'd sold most of her jewelry.

Joséphine wrote to Tremplier at least once a day. In November 1897 her letters to him suddenly stopped. He wrote. No response. He sent telegrams. Nothing. A frantic note to her concierge said: "If you haven't seen her, force the door. She may have come to harm."

Madame Boron remembers last seeing Joséphine around noon on 19 November, when she'd returned from one of her journeys. "After lunch, send your niece," she had said. "I want her to hem my red peignoir. I need it today. I'm having a bath. A client is coming later." Around three the niece knocked. Hearing no answer, she left. Ten days of letters piled up outside the prostitute's door, but the concierge was used to these inexplicable absences.

Tremplier's letter suggested something urgent. Madame Boron showed it to the police commissioner, who broke into the whore's apartment and followed the stench of putrefaction to its source. Joséphine lay on the bedroom floor, her peignoir pushed above the waist. There was no sign of struggle. Just a clean bullet hole in her head and bloody foam on her lips.

Chief detective Cochefert was the next to arrive. He verified she'd been dead about a week by examining her mail. The oldest letter, dated 19 November, had come in the fourth daily delivery, between twelve-thirty and two-thirty, suggesting a date and time of the crime.

* * *

Late November of 1897 was unusually cold. A thick, persistent fog made Parisians think of London. Shopkeepers had to light the gas to do their morning business. Boats servicing the Seine were forced to drop their passengers at the nearest landing and moor there until the fog cleared. The day after Joséphine Bigot was found, Rodot was in his apartment, reading the newspaper by candlelight.

The front page of *Le Figaro* was dominated by two letters reproduced in facsimile, concerning the Dreyfus affair. The handwriting of Esterhazy was being compared to that of an incriminating, treasonous letter, purported to have been written by Captain Dreyfus, now rotting on Devil's Island. The writing of the two letters, subjected to the analysis of a specialist, was exactly the same. Paris was being asked to draw its own conclusions. The traitor was clearly not Dreyfus but Esterhazy himself. By comparison, news of Joséphine Bigot's murder, which ordinarily would have entertained the population of thirty-six million French citizens, was hardly noticed, except by criminologists. Rodot clipped out the article on the prostitute and underlined certain passages in red.

* * *

Next morning Bertillon came to photograph the crime. The apartment was black. The fog had turned day into night. He lit a candle and saw the mannish body of a woman with livid green flesh, dressed in red. He lit an oil lamp on the mantel and placed the candle near it, exploding flash at intervals during the exposure. Flash was always unkind. It raked over the victim's possessions, exposing dirt and neglect. Its cruel truth would have made a murdered whore seem to deserve her fate. Bertillon's picture shows Joséphine bloated and abandoned. Even in his flash, her rooms are spotless.

The photographer also shot the *cabinet de toilette* because the last time Joséphine was seen alive she told her concierge she was going to have a bath. Arranging the camera to place the bidet in the middle of the frame, Bertillon included the piano. Later, as he developed the image, an assistant accidently burst in, flooding the dark room with light. Bertillon regarded the result as a ruin, but it went into the files as it was.

Robbery wasn't the motive. Despite claims of the recent sale of her jewels, Cochefert found a gold and turquoise necklace, assorted rings, watches, silver salt spoons, and a crucifix. The stock certificates were also untouched. He found Joséphine's correspondence on the bed. The killer had gone through the letters, evidently to extract his own. On a table, a postcard addressed to Joséphine caught Cochefert's attention: that's how the murderer introduced himself into the house, he thought.

Cochefert wonders how many murderers of prostitutes there are on the loose. He considers Joséphine Bigot, the mannish whore who wrapped in ribbons letters from men applying to fuck her. He examines them all. Most are signed with untraceable codes or initials. He ignores one signed "Rodot."

By late January 1898, Cochefert, without any suspects, is visited by a former omnibus conductor named Franger. "Whoever killed Joséphine Bigot wasn't just practicing. Years back, my old friend Rodot wrote anonymous letters to the police saying he killed Marie Jouin, the big, beautiful blonde on the Rue Condorcet. It wouldn't surprise me if he had something to do with Bigot."

"Why are you coming forward now?"

"Too many of these women are dying."

The Jouin murder was fourteen years before. A ten-year statute of limitations makes the case too old for Cochefert to legally nail this "friend" of Franger. He goes to the Rue de l'Arc-de-Triomphe and arrests him anyway. On its front page *Le Petit Journal* publishes a line drawing of Rodot from one of Bertillon's "talking" portraits. The press loves former detectives suspected of murder: "Agent-Assassin arrested!"

Rodot's amused. He knows he can't be held responsible for a fourteen-year-old crime. As for Bigot, "I never knew her."

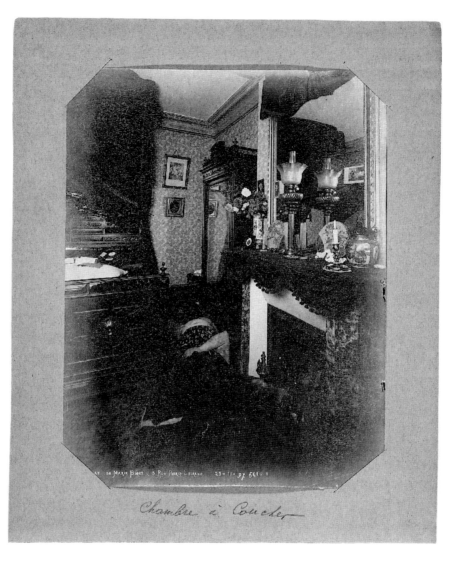

Chambre à Coucher

MURDER OF MARIE BIGOT, 3 RUE PIERRE-LE-GRAND, 28. II. 97

Bedroom

MARIE BIGOT AFFAIR

Cabinet de toilette

Cochefert searches the suspect's room and finds it full of boxes of letters responding to his advertisements offering protective services to women and widows with fortunes. More than a thousand letters are from prostitutes. He has Joséphine's friend Tremplier look through them. The engineer finds nothing like her writing.

Cochefert goes through his predecessor Macé's papers and finds Rodot's anonymous letters about the whore Jouin. The writing is the same as that of a letter signed "Rodot" in Joséphine's suitcases. He grills the suspect for hours. "With all respect to a fellow detective, this is idiotic! A letter from me doesn't prove I killed her! Show me real evidence, and we'll discuss it."

Cochefert's convinced that Rodot not only killed Jouin and Bigot but many of the others. He has no grounds whatever to prosecute.

Rodot's protectress, the old marquise, has begun to lose confidence in him. She starts giving Cochefert information. "He had a revolver in the house, which I insisted he get rid of. He said he sent it to a friend in Brussels. I can give you his name." Cochefert finds the revolver. It uses the same size bullets as the one in Joséphine's skull. "You're laughable!" Cochefert takes Rodot before the concierge. He brings him to the hospital where the niece is sick with bronchitis. Neither woman recognizes him.

Cochefert points to the newspaper articles, carefully annotated by Rodot in red: "We're detectives, addicted to the chase. How could I not be interested in all mysterious crimes? Plenty of people do the same thing. Does it mean we're guilty?"

"But he locked up the papers about Bigot. He didn't lock up his other business," says the marquise.

"That's crazy. Let him prove I'm guilty!"

In mid-January, another whore, Léontine Caluras, forty-five, called "The Scooter," who specialized in rolling drunks, is found murdered in a furnished room at 8 Rue Royer-Collard. Cochefert has no leads on her either. He's absorbed by Bigot and the glorified pimp, who may have known one another. Or maybe not. The seals are removed from Joséphine's apartment. All her goods are sold at auction, her family in Brittany not having responded to any of the examining magistrate's many letters.

"We can't touch him," Cochefert told reporters. Nonetheless, Rodot was jailed for over two months, during which he made copious notes on his case in preparation for a colossal law suit. Finally, on 1 April, he was released, pale, but elegantly dressed.

"I'm free, really free," he told reporters.

"Did you kill Marie Jouin?"

"One says so many things. Wait ten years," he smiled. "I'll tell you if I killed Bigot. Until then, the marquise and I are changing apartments. The wagging tongues in our neighborhood are too long."

10 Fat and Ashes

30 November 1897, 7 Rue Etienne Dolet, village of Kremlin-Bicêtre, south of Paris, Augustin-Frédéric Lamarre, 65, retired railway worker and bank messenger for the Comptoir National d'Escompte, struck dead with a carriage key and completely incinerated by Xavier-Ange Carrara, 35, mushroom grower. Sentenced to death 25 May 1898. Guillotined 25 June 1898. His wife and accomplice, Louise-Julie Roëlandt Carrara, 24, sentenced to forced labor for life.

He burrows, planting spores in decaying manure, filling every cranny of his wrecked quarry with *blanc de champignon*—mycelium, downy and virgin blue-white. Shoring up hay along the landslides, packing cesspools, he's covered in urine, sawdust, horse droppings. The smells are inseparable from his own. They comfort him, give him hope. He crouches, breathing the spermy musk of mushroom spawn. He hears it spreading through the stony labyrinth.

The first mushroom appears, a star in a moonless night sky. A thousand more caps poke through, tiny lights that seem like a firmament above the flame of his torch. He joins their intelligence. They breathe him.

The spores are eternal, older than the universe. His existence is a fierce effort to prove himself against their tricks. When the beds blister with caps that get no bigger than a pea and shrivel up, a voice tells him they're bewitched. He stabs at rats, scalds mites and wood-lice with boiling water. He checks the ventilation that rids the caves of poisonous gas — fumes of rat excrement, impurities that enter on his workers' clothing and shoes — through the air shafts from the yard outside his house. He worries about iron. The tiniest particles have the power to stop mushroom growth absolutely. He thinks a workman had only to slip along the beds with a pocket of rusty nails and insert them here and there to render the spawn inert and destroy him.

Absorbed by the secrets of the earth, he puts aside names and meanings. He forgets his origins, his mother in Italy, the commune of Neuilly-Plaisance, inhabited by stone cutters and mushroom growers, all from Albano, where his brothers taught him to grow White Buttons, *Agaricus campestris.* "Parisians eat them like bread," they said. He's lost track of these brothers now growing mushrooms in New York. He's joined a fraternity of the blind. When he climbs above ground, he's as cranky as an ousted mole.

* * *

Xavier Carrara, renderer of rot into mushrooms, shares a house above his caves in Kremlin-Bicêtre, south of Paris, with a wife, three children, and a father-in-law. The region along the Bièvre River is a miasma of tanners and leather workers who scrape the flesh from sheep and rabbit skins, which they soften with alum and sell to glove makers. His neighbors raise horses and cattle. They sell the fat of their slaughtered beasts to be turned into tallow and soap. The atmosphere of transformation has stunted the growth of the entire population between the Porte d'Italie and the town of Fontainebleau. All survive on dust and soot, on what dogs trail from their mouths, on whatever they can find: animal parts, the remains of perished things fluttering

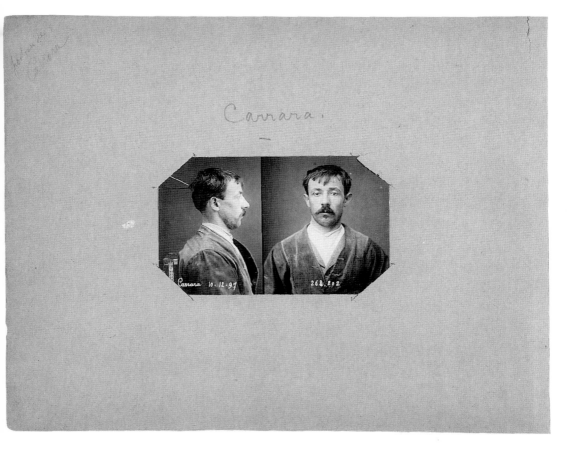

Carrara

CARRARA

AFFAIR CARRARA

House of Carrara, 7 Rue Etienne Dolet in Kremlin-Bicêtre, 11. 12. 97
Murder of Lamarre

in the wind. When a mushroom crop aborts, Carrara tells his wife, "If I don't get some money, we'll rot here with everything else."

Tormented by failures, he becomes the prey of great projects. Visions of fire give him courage. Twice he sets fire to his carriage and collects 700 francs in damages. He plans to burn down his stable, leading the good horse into the yard, leaving the blind one in a stall. "It's old and sick. We need to replace it," he says.

While he and his cart driver hitch the good horse and go to Villejuif with a crop of mushrooms, his wife pours kerosene on the hay and tosses in a match. Sickened by the moans of the blind horse suffocating from the smoke, she stands holding her ears, thinking she'll go mad, wanting to flee as the building explodes. Later, neighbors behind their curtains watch her and Carrara drag the carbonized horse from the ruins. They see the couple gesticulating to an agent from the Aigle Insurance Company who holds a handkerchief to his nose. The Carraras collect 2,300 francs.

There were other dark doings. Carrara and some mushroom growers don't like leaving their caves to make regular Paris deliveries. They elected one grower to take in all their baskets. Once this messenger stopped at a tavern and got drunk, forgetting his satchel with all the growers' money in a carriage he was too muddled to find. Hearing the bad news, Carrara got up in the middle of the night, rode his bicycle to the tavern, searched the parked carriages, and found the one with the forgotten satchel. It contained 700 francs in small coins. He pedaled home and slipped into bed. Accepting the grower's apologetic repayment of his share of the loss, he added it to the stolen money he'd hidden in a cupboard.

* * *

When Julie Carrara burned down their stable she felt like the heroine of a tale with a happy ending. She loves the way people behave in stories. She reads to her husband from serials in the newspaper. In *La Fille sans dot* (*The Girl without a Dowry*), a maid drugs a suitor to steal his money. How easy it is to commit crimes without leaving a trace, Carrara thinks. How like mushrooms certain poisons are. Some are tasteless. They leave no sediment at the bottom of the glass and don't change the color of the drink. Forming a plan, his confidence over-flowed. At a card game he told his father-in-law, "Anyone comes carrying 40,000 francs, he won't leave alive. You do a job well, there's nothing to worry about."

Carrara is shrunken and brown. Julie, much younger, is fat and rosy with pale, pig's eyes. Fine blonde hair surrounds her face. She could be the sister of La Goulue, the dancing glutton who outraged the crowds at the Moulin Rouge. Julie Carrara doesn't particularly like her husband, but she loves intrigue. She used to do laundry and clean houses, but prefers hanging around dance halls where she flirts with customers so they'll spend money on her. Everyone calls her "The Mushroom Kid" or "Champignonne," variant of "Mignon," a name for all nameless whores. Her reputation was no secret to Carrara when he married her.

Every appetite creates its world. Julie claims to fear Carrara's temper, but his schemes excite her. He suspects she's sleeping with their cart driver but hides his jealousy by turning her habits to profit. He takes her to dance halls around Villejuif to meet patrons.

The Carraras rouse themselves with fantasies about crimes. They owe 178 francs to the Crédit Lyonnais and decide, when the bank messenger comes to collect, they'll take his money after shooting him with a pistol. They drop the idea when they realize the messenger, who starts his rounds in Gentilly, won't have gathered enough worth stealing by the time he reaches their house. They also owe seventy-five francs to the Comptoir National d'Escompte. They could kill this mes-senger who would have started from farther away and be carrying more money. "Kill him, or you're no man," Julie taunts. He hasn't the balls to pull this off, she tells herself. He blinks at her.

* * *

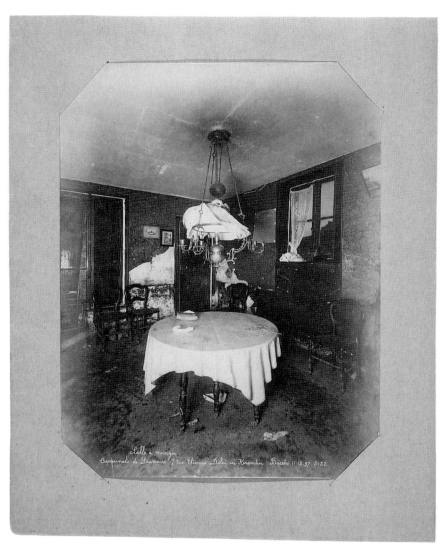

DINING ROOM

Murder of Lamarre, 7 Rue Etienne Dolet in Kremlin-Bicêtre, 11. 12. 97

The landscape around the Carrara house conceals miles of stone and plaster quarries. Their interior replicates this dank underworld. A ferret might have dug out the dining room. It has filthy, broken windows. Chairs sway against walls of scarred plaster smeared with soot. The floor around the table is a path of rancid food, all the more bizarre for the presence of a silver-handled brush for collecting crumbs. A brass lamp with a petticoat and candle sconces hangs from a pulley overhead. Lamp smoke clouds the ceiling, completing the dwelling of troglodytes.

The bank messenger of the Comptoir National d'Escompte hesitates before entering. Everything about the house offends his sense of decency. He gags at the odor. He tries not to stare at the wallpaper succumbing to its own weight in the humidity, the dubious tablecloth, the greasy crumb brush — travesties of Parisian gentility. "Collect their money, say thank-you, and get out," he murmurs.

He's Augustin-Frédéric Lamarre, sixty-five. He's been married for nearly half a century. No one has ever seen him drunk. He retired after forty years with the Compagnie des Chemins de Fer de l'Ouest. To keep busy he collects bank notes two days a week to supplement an inheritance from his mother. He wears a big white mustache, a skull cap edged in black imitation-lambskin, and a hooded pilgrim's cape, resembling those worn by policemen. He's tall and strong, heavy, but not obese. He keeps his mother's wedding ring on a silk cord around his neck.

The Carraras decided a pistol would make too much noise. Behind the dining-room door they placed a huge iron key for tightening the nuts in carriage wheels. As Lamarre searches his satchel for their bill, Julie excuses herself. On the stairs to their bedroom, she signals her husband. Carrara grabs the carriage key with both hands, creeps behind Lamarre, and clubs him.

They take the strap from his bag, bind him, drag the body to the kitchen, and cover it with a tarp. Later, Carrara moves it to the coal room while Julie spreads the money under the lamp. She counts

22,734 francs and five centimes. "I've never seen so much!" Carrara cries. To avert suspicion he borrows 150 francs from a neighbor, claiming he needs it to pay another bank.

Their children return from school. Julie wipes Lamarre's blood from the floor and has them play in the dining room, while Carrara drags the body to the air shaft of the quarry. He ropes it to the wheel of a manure barrel, hiding it in the space between the shaft and the wooden cone that covers the opening. Julie gives the children a quick supper and sends them to bed.

* * *

"Light the brazier before you leave, papa!" Carrara yells down to his father-in-law. It's a normal request. Mushroom growers ventilate their galleries with huge fires. The older man and a worker mount and go to a café. Carrara and Julie suspend the body in the shaft on a cable, keeping it there during dinner. When everyone is in bed Carrara enters the cave on a ladder and lowers the bank messenger, head-first, into the white-hot brazier.

Carrara has carbonized nearly every known substance, but he's never burned a human being before. He isn't frightened. He's thrilled. At first, the flesh sputters. Then the skull explodes, spraying his face and clothes. Glistening with fat, he surrenders completely to the task, adding coal, breaking the head with a poker until it's reduced to ashes. He lowers the body further to burn the torso, dodging explosions from the combusting flesh. He pokes, adds more coal, lowers the body again. Pieces of the bank messenger fly in all directions. Carrara chases bones, muscle and fat, picking them up, scraping them off the walls and floor of the cave, flinging them back into the fire.

He's sweating, running, lost in the sport of converting Lamarre. He's toiled miserably all his life, but he's never worked as hard as during this night. He's ecstatic, delirious in the grandeur of the flames. He can't help laughing out loud. He feels thirsty. Several times he stops and climbs the ladder, crosses the yard to the kitchen and gulps a glass of wine. Calmed by the alcohol, he returns, tending the body like a giant brush fire, rendering every bit of it to dust.

It takes him eight hours. The time means nothing to him. Poking the embers he discovers things the flames won't transform: Lamarre's hernia bandage, gold from his watch, buckles from his trousers and shoes, a copper matchbox, metal closures of satchel and wallet. He buries these throughout the caves. Then he takes Lamarre's ashes and like a sower, broadcasts them over the mushroom beds, following a peasant's instinct to waste nothing.

He returns to his wife, drunk, his eyes burning with joy. His hair and clothes are plastered with fat. "You stink like a tanner!" She rolls over.

* * *

For the next few days they live as if nothing happened. A bank messenger arrives from the Crédit Lyonnais. They pay and let him go. Carrara jokes with his carpenter. "One blow to the nape of your neck, and I could down you." The couple goes to the Tête Noire music hall and dance together, looking for customers for Julie.

The newspapers are printing articles about a missing bank messenger called Lamarre. His wife describes his clothes and personal habits to the police, adding that he has a slight nick on the upper part of his left ear. The police interview the clients on his list which takes them to the Carraras' door.

Chief of Criminal Investigation Cochefert arrives. He's prepared to spend hours pounding the couple with questions. At first, they're mute. They've seen no one. But then their four-year-old daughter, Hélène, steps forward, "A man got sick in our house and couldn't move." Cochefert thanks the child. Julie pushes her out of the room in a panic, then screams at the detective, "Don't look at *me*! He did it!"

"She *pushed me* into it!" Carrara coughs mucus and tears. "She signaled me from the stairs. She wiped up the blood. She helped me drag the body to the shaft!" The confession is a family brawl.

VENTILATION SHAFT

Murder of Lamarre, 7 Rue Etienne Dolet in Kremlin-Bicêtre, 11. 12. 97

Cochefert asks Carrara to re-enact the crime, noticing he mimes it with extraordinary freedom and spirit, jumping ahead of the questions. Just as suddenly, he becomes morose. Cochefert's afraid he'll commit suicide. When agents take him to the caves to complete his story, they lash him to a stool and lower him like a package. "I did a good job of it!" he yells from midair. "I told you. He's entirely burned. Poor guy. Nothing's left. Turn my quarry inside out. You won't find a trace of him. Raise up the murderer!" he bellows, and they hoist him to the surface.

* * *

The investigating magistrate doesn't believe in murder without a body or in crime scenes he can't plot and measure. Carrara's an Italian, which suggests a race of wild men, sword-wielding anarchists, like Santo Caserio, who murdered the President of the Republic three years ago. A low-life mushroom grower isn't smart enough to make someone disappear.

The magistrate brings in a mining engineer, a mushroom specialist, a toxicologist, a corps of experts in subterranean excavation. He enlists mushroom workers from Carrara's neighborhood. In lamp light agents join the dwarfs of Kremlin-Bicêtre and crawl through the caves, digging with pickaxes, searching for bones and clothing, driving the rats into deeper hiding places.

They find the iron closing of Lamarre's satchel in a crevasse, in another, his hernia bandage and part of his watch. They find a box of money behind a stone marked "15." They're convinced the victim is in a cesspool or at the bottom of a deep shaft. The diggers destroy the entire farm and don't find a bone. Forced to call Carrara's success "singular," they all but praise his "incredible tenacity."

In Paris a practical joker leaves a basket of mushrooms and live frogs outside Cochefert's office. The note reads simply: "Find Lamarre." Cochefert ponders this as a message from the citizens of Paris. Lamarre is exactly what he can't find. The chief detective is famous for

VENTILATION SHAFT

Murder of Lamarre, 7 Rue Etienne Dolet in Kremlin-Bicêtre, 11.12.97

BRAZIER

Murder of Lamarre, 7 Rue Etienne Dolet in Kremlin-Bicêtre, 11. 12. 97

PLACE WHERE THE BOX CONTAINING THE BANK NOTES AND GOLD WAS FOUND

Murder of Lamarre, 7 Rue Etienne Dolet in Kremlin–Bicêtre, 11. 12. 97

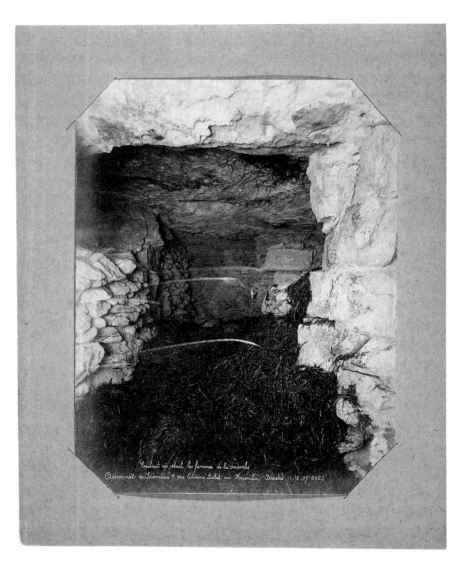

PLACE WHERE THE METAL FITTINGS OF THE SATCHEL WERE FOUND

Murder of Lamarre, 7 Rue Etienne Dolet in Kremlin-Bicêtre, 11.12.97

piecing together crimes from nothing at all. In Carrara he's met a cunning trickster. Brushing his clothes after hours underground, Cochefert not only dusts off Lamarre. He carries him home on his shoes.

* * *

One of Bertillon's assistants from the Anthropometric Service comes to take the required photographs. He descends into the pit and makes views where the searchers found the unburned remains. He explodes magnesium to illuminate the impossible terrain, supplementing these timed blasts with gentler, defining light from small oil lamps, placed here and there, to point up details. During the long exposures he moves these lamps. In the images the trails look like shooting stars.

The photographer also records the brazier. He shows it next to a poker and piece of rope. The grate looks too small to have held a combusting human being. The picture reveals nothing of the ferocity of the crime. Its meaning depends entirely on the story.

The crime photographed lacks everything important: flames, suspended corpse, Carrara, agent of the Devil. The pictures are only to remind the jury of the unthinkable. The lawyers will add the fact that Lamarre, composted, occupies nearly a mile of caves and tunnels. By contrast, staff artists for *Le Petit Journal* describe Carrara's feat in special color supplements. They portray the mushroom grower and his wife posing at home. They invent a scene for each phase of the drama, culminating in the Italian ghoul and his suspended victim, phosphorescent against the brazier.

Excited by the illustrations, Parisians hire carriages to visit Kremlin-Bicêtre. There's no other reason to come to this reeking wasteland. The visitors find a street musician near the house, singing couplets that celebrate the crime. He sells them in broadsheets as souvenirs.

* * *

The authorities insist on their theory. The body is intact, buried somewhere. It was not incinerated, nor has it vanished. They will show this to be physically impossible. Science will smash Carrara's claims of super-human powers. It will reveal him as he really is, a cretin, a monster consumed by greed. To make the point the toxicologist burns a goat:

"After three or four hours, the body is merely roasted. Incineration hasn't even begun," he reports. "Cremation has several phases: liquids, blood, and humors vaporize; the body dries; fat and conjunctive tissue fuse; muscles calcify until all that remains is bony tissue, which always resists complete incineration. Flat bones like the shoulder blades, and long bones of the legs and arms submit to vitrification. With the shaft measuring twenty-five to thirty meters the Italian could have produced the heat, but in eight hours he never could have burned the body in the way he said."

When the toxicologist analyzes the ashes in Carrara's brazier he finds no trace of organic debris. The mining engineer analyzes the earth around it for fat. Nothing. Chief detective Cochefert marvels at the lack of evidence. These professional doubters seem planted in the audience of Carrara's magic show. Their denials and exasperation only magnify the triumph of the illusion.

* * *

Waiting trial in Mazas prison, Carrara wrote letters, which the newspapers, maintaining the popular clamor, printed. "Dear cousin. Use my bicycle. I don't need it. And bring me wine, a four-pound loaf of bread, Gruyère cheese, some fruit, and a fifty-centime pack of tobacco." Carrara received only bread and onions. "He's mocking me. I'm here dying of hunger, while he's in my cellar drinking all the beer and wine." The irony of little agonies over food by the man who roasted Lamarre escaped no one.

The mushroom cultivator-assassin, dragged from his habitat, lost his glamour in the halls of justice. Reporters at the trial likened the blue velour suit he wore to that of a game warden. He burrowed in his chair, hardly visible behind the balustrade. Julie, in black, covered her pale hair with a mantilla. When her father testified, she wouldn't stop screaming. A doctor gave her cordials and ether.

There were many spring storms. At midday the courtroom was so dark that for the first time the newly-installed electric lights were used in the Assizes. The attendance rippled with pleasure as the little bulbs, bursting into brightness, lit the vaults of the chambers. Carrara looked up, puzzled, and thought of mushrooms.

After the couple were sentenced, Julie's father offered to raise Xavier and Hélène, the two elder children. A brother of Carrara took baby Georges.

* * *

Carrara hoped for an appeal. He showed great piety, ate with good appetite, played cards, laughed with his guards, slept well, and turned the pages of Italian books. His only rages were against his wife, whom, he insisted until the end, "sold" him. "If I'm pardoned and go to New Caledonia, I'll divorce her and take the kids with me so I can watch them grow up."

On the day of his execution, rain kept most people away. One hundred and fifty foot soldiers and fifty mounted guards were the largest group in attendance. A few whores, pimps, and other night stalkers mingled with reporters around the scaffold.

No one claimed the body. A grave was prepared in the section of the Ivry Cemetery where they bury executed criminals. But returning the mushroom grower to the earth had to wait. After a few prayers, a delegate from the Faculty of Medicine conducted the body to the dissecting theater for the instruction of students. The place bore a certain resemblance to Carrara's neighborhood of tanners and soap makers. There, as along the Bièvre, someone would undoubtedly re-gard the immolator as material to be rendered into saleable parts be-fore the state ploughed him under.

11 Breath

20–21 January 1898, 234 Rue Curial,
XIXth Arrondissement, Théophile Cadet-
Liévin, 67, night watchman at the La Villette
gasworks, robbed, beaten, and stabbed
to death. Several gasworkers arrested,
questioned, and released for lack of evidence.

The gasworks of La Villette is a stinking envelope on the northern margin of Paris. Here soft coal is burned into gas, which enters the city through a network of mains. At the turn of a knob, jets explode in streets and houses into the evil-fingered, tremulous flames of gaslight.

La Villette is a world of the dead. Workers, stunted from the poisonous haze, are shades. Remnants of a race long extinct, they drift through the vast spaces, enter hangars, mount ladders on mammoth cylindrical gasometers, ride railroad cars that transport the coal. Their rudimentary eyes are those of blind fish addressing vague questions, to no one in particular.

Théophile Cadet-Liévin pedaled his bicycle to the gasworks for forty years. He perceived his diminishment, from human being to shadow, gradually. Smoke made stinging slits of his eyes. He clumsily brushed away the tears, trying to avoid hitting the other automatons wheeling to work past the crucifix on the Rue de l'Evangile. Mucus at the back of his throat was an asphalt soup. He imagined tar permanently staining his guts, and thought, with certain dread, that turned inside out he'd be indistinguishable from the morbid filth around him.

* * *

Certain festivities restored the gasworks to historical times. The events were aeronautical, because of the availability of coal gas which filled a balloon faster than hydrogen. It was also slower to escape. Théophile Cadet-Liévin wasn't interested in these practical matters. The ascents from La Villette pierced him with longing, inspired a mania for lightness. He had a passion to slip through the melancholy ceiling of the factory and float in an unending expanse of blue. Like the first French aristocratic aeronauts, he saw ballooning less as sport than a form of redemption. "They'll discover how to avoid death," he thought.

The conviction came from a dream he had as a child. He was walking down a street when he noticed a car dangling from its balloon by a single rope. The rope supported a large hook that swept along the paving stones like an iron predator. He tried to flee. The menacing claw pierced him, entering above the left knee, reemerging through his right thigh. Solidly skewered, he felt no pain. Nor was he dizzy or faint. The balloon rose a thousand feet. His neighbors turned into crazed ants. Meadows, haystacks, and curving rivers spread before him like embroidery. He prayed. He shouted for help. Hours went by. The balloon began to descend. He whirled around. So did all the people below.

"Help me my friends! Or I'm lost!" he cried.

"Never fear. We'll save you!" they called back. He landed in a pile of hay, still alive. The farmers released him, and he was carried to the arms of his mother.

He never spoke of the dream, but it determined his opinions. He was an indignant member of the crowd when *Le Géant* rose over the Champ de Mars. Its car was the size of a bungalow. Its stylish passengers threw empty champagne bottles and glasses onto the crowd below. He wondered if any real need to transcend earthly cares lay behind the great photographer-aeronaut Nadar's puffed-up showmanship. To Cadet balloon flight was a silent voyage of solitary trust in the wind. It was not the balloon which traveled, but air itself. Lift-off was the ascent of the Holy Spirit. One day a balloon would take him from the gasworks into the Kingdom of Heaven.

* * *

During the siege of Paris in 1870, the Prussian army cut communications to and from the city. Cadet witnessed more than sixty different balloon ascents—attempts to contact the world outside. Men of magical daring piloted the vessels, former sailors, merchants, engineers, chemists, writers, and gymnasts. Not unlike himself, he fancied, they were ready to risk their lives for the noble purpose of carrying, in a single voyage, hundreds of thousands of letters and visiting cards to people separated from loved ones. He longed to enter the car and rise above the Tuileries gardens, Boulevard d'Italie, Montmartre and share the exultation of the smiling aeronauts, haloed in opaline vapor, waving handkerchiefs as they floated over the trees.

Two of the siege balloons originated from La Villette. Cadet pushed through the crowd to touch the flexible wicker and net, to caress the twilled taffeta treated with gutta percha, thousands of meters of which seamstresses had assembled for the envelope. *Les Etats-Unis* expanded from a monstrous pile of fabric into the taut globe that bore Nadar's assistant, veteran aeronaut Louis Godard, toward Mantes with fifty-eight kilograms of letters. René Cuzon ascended in *La Bretagne* for a three-hour flight to Verdun, only to be captured by the Prussians. These were balloons of hope. The sky ships, bearing carrier pigeons that would fly messages back, filled Cadet with unspeakable ecstasy. When he learned that all but eight of the siege balloons had reached their destinations, he forgot his supper, gazed out of his attic window, and wept.

After the Franco-Prussian war he watched the *Zénith* rise from the gasworks through a pool of sunlight. Its mission was to measure the tolerance of human lungs for higher altitudes. The aeronauts, Sivel, Crocé-Spinelli, and Tissandier, used oxygen-fed respiratory machines to breathe. Drifting into the cirrus, they attained 28,000 feet. At ten degrees below zero, Sivel and Crocé-Spinelli turned black. Paralyzed and vomiting blood, they lost consciousness. The ship landed near Arcachon. Peasants found them dead near their overturned car. Tissandier survived to publish the story of his companions' ghastly asphyxiation, an illustrated version of which Cadet devoured in the newspapers.

He was also entranced by the *Aérocycle,* a double balloon, to which an acrobat calling himself "The Gladiator" attached a tightrope. The artist danced on the wire, leaping onto a suspended bicycle. Pedaling his own bicycle Théophile followed the *Aérocycle*'s huge shadow in a slow path westward from La Villette into his own neighborhood. He heard the ship heaving like a gigantic lung, hovering above the rooftops, and watched it crash on the Rue Marcadet, precisely where the street intersected the Rue des Poissonniers, where he lived. The Gladiator flew into the air. Cadet joined the mob that scrambled onto a rooftop to try and save him. Steadying himself, he gazed down on pickpockets working the crowd.

* * *

Certain crimes occur in shadow worlds which cannot be surveyed, for which there is no vantage point. The thick atmosphere and empty spaces of La Villette encouraged little rituals of unmasked hatred among the workers, not unlike those of a penal colony. As a young man, Cadet, who was rather small, was often the chosen victim. They'd knock him down, take his money or bicycle, and watch his frustration as he searched for what he thought he'd lost. Then with crooked smiles, they'd return the possessions. These human ghosts devised more sinister plots at the gasworks, for it was not really a place but a cloud into which culprits could simply evaporate.

Affaire du père Cadet
Vue du hangar où le cadavre a été découvert

MURDER OF CADET, RUE CURIAL, 21. 1. 98

Père Cadet affair

View of the enclosure where the body was found

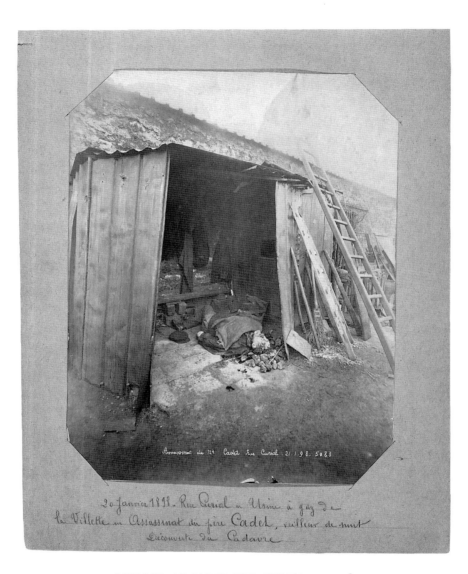

MURDER OF CADET, RUE CURIAL, 21. I. 98

20 January 1898, Rue Curial, gasworks of La Villette
Murder of *père* Cadet, night watchman
Discovery of the body

When Cadet became too old to do his regular job he was made a night watchman. By then the jokes had ceased. His tormentors were gone. He thought of his sentry box as a balloon car. Paid to sit alone, he gazed at the sky, guarding nothing he could name.

In late January it was dark by four-thirty. On the eve of St Agnes Cadet waited for the appearance of Mercury, enthralled as the stars gradually became visible, pulsing in infinitesimal movements of worlds beyond worlds. He had the whole night ahead of him. It was still and cold. Snug in two pairs of trousers, he chewed on his pipe. The sixty-five francs he was paid every other Thursday were in his pocket.

Whispers in the dark. A voice from the sentry post opposite. But the watchman there had already gone. Cadet stood alone in the yard and wondered, listening again for the sounds that had interrupted his solitude. A blow, and he fell. Shadows slit his throat, unbuttoned both pairs of trousers to empty them of his money, grabbed the watch in his vest, and flung his coat into a pit.

* * *

When Cadet's replacement arrived early in the morning, he saw a sleeper in the doorway of the guard box and, raising his lantern, recognized the old worker. Blood was frozen in rivulets along his face. A huge pool came from a gash hidden under his long scarf. Like the fallen aeronauts of the *Zénith,* black from lack of oxygen, Cadet's expression was that of amazement.

Bertillon arrived with his camera and photographed the body and the shanty. He made a wide-angle view of the yard, trying to impose geometrical logic that would appear to chart the space and expose the probabilities of the acts that had taken place. He'd been applying this system to crime interiors. He thought he could aid investigations if his pictures reconstituted the shape of a room, by reflecting the exact distances between the pieces of furniture. The idea was impressive, another example of Bertillon's conceit. But it was a false precision no one could interpret. For months police agents stared at the photographs but La Villette was unknowable, a perpetual twilight.

Chief of Criminal Investigation Cochefert filled the gasworks with informants and agents dressed as workers. They immediately arrested three suspects. There was no evidence these men had committed the crime. Like La Villette itself, all was rumor. Cochefert took them to the prefecture, had them stripped naked, and grilled them for twenty-four hours. The newspapers didn't report what happened at these sessions. They liked picturesque details, the famous "tobacco bonus" an agent would get for extracting a confession, not the beatings that brought it about. They didn't report that the treatment was useless on the workers of La Villette.

* * *

In late January 1898 no one was interested in the death of a night watchman. Zola dominated the press with "J'accuse," the anarchist Georges Etiévant had dynamited two police agents on the Rue Berzélius, and a man and wife, domestics who'd just buried a newborn, were found asphyxiated by carbon monoxide from a faulty stove.

The spirit of Cadet departed in a small balloon. "I've been insensible," he observed, removing his long scarf and dropping ballast as the car surmounted the gasworks' leaden ceiling. He drifted over the Saint-Denis canal, skirted the slaughter houses, and followed the Ourcq canal eastward, guided by Mercury, the only planet visible on the night the shades tried to overtake him.

12 The Sailboat

9 May 1898, 37 Rue Poissonnière,
IInd Arrondissement, Louis-Joseph Banderly, 26,
dentist, murdered and robbed by
Albert-Hilaire Martin, 17, dental technician,
who used a monkey wrench to try
and kill Madame Campredon, 27, cashier.
Sentenced to forced labor for life.

When Albert Martin used to ride his bicycle along the quays on Sundays, he always turned into the Tuileries to watch the photographers around the puppet theater. Everything he saw there was a vision of modern elegance. Fashionable ladies primped in the sunshine, clicking each other with little black boxes. The gentlemen were more serious. They had tripods and dark cloths. They were his heroes, the masters he wanted to emulate.

"No! Not again!" The beak-nosed puppet is whining, fending off his wife's terrible blows.

"Yes! Hit him again!" The hag whacks his hump with her mallet as the audience dissolves in laughter. The photographers are ready. They uncap their lenses on the glorious day, the ragtag actors, and the children, transported by the magic of the performance.

Albert wheeled his cycle along the gravel paths finding, in the chestnut trees, another camera operator, shuffling this way and that under his shroud, waiting for a dog to pass or a parasol to close before exposing his plate on a family, tinted green by the luminous canopy.

The boy thinks of his parents and sister on the Rue de Navarin. His mother is the concierge of their building. His father spends Sundays waxing the hallways. They save their money and sit sternly reading the newspaper or gossiping about their neighbors. If he had a camera he used to think, he'd invite them to stroll in the fresh air, have them breathe the rosy perfumes of the parks where he'd arrange them to look like other families.

Albert Martin, blond and small, looks much younger than seventeen. He lives at home, returning promptly each night for soup under waning gaslight. Sometimes he visits the library and turns the pages of the illustrated magazines or ponders headlines in *Le Petit Journal*. For months he followed the case of Carrara, the mushroom grower who murdered a bank messenger, stuffed him down a shaft, and reduced him to ashes.

Albert suffered hallucinations as a child. This deprived him of a proper education, but he managed to become a laboratory technician by apprenticing with several dentists. They found him a good worker, which delighted his parents, since they anguished in secret over the fate of their sickly boy. Albert gives them his entire salary. He'd like to photograph their surprise when they find the wages he slips each week under his mother's napkin.

Working for Dr Hutin, a dentist on the Rue de l'Arbre-Sec, Albert stole fifty francs from the cash drawer. Since he'd never committed a crime before, Hutin didn't prosecute or ask to be repaid. He simply fired him.

Albert spent the money on a camera, dark cloth, tripod, and plates. He joined the amateurs near the puppet show. He took portraits of his friends and of himself standing by his bicycle. He photographed the wind in the trees, a lemonade seller, children chasing hoops or launching model yachts on vast wading pools. Once when he photographed one of these boats and its reflection, he turned the

MURDER OF BANDERLY, BOULVARD POISSONIÈRE, 10. 5. 98

9 May 1898, murder of Banderly, dentist, by Martin, Hilaire, his apprentice
Discovery of the body in the studio

picture upside-down, preferring the wavy version of the vessel to its clearer counterpart.

"That's stupid," said his friend Jean Balloche. "Turn it the right way."

"It's more beautiful my way. This isn't a regular boat. The blur of the shadows makes it look like it's travelling to far-away places." Albert was hypnotized by his dream.

"A boat's a boat," Balloche insisted.

"Not on the water. The reflection changes it." Balloche shrugged. He didn't know what Albert was talking about.

After his failure with Hutin, Albert found work with another dentist but was let go for what this doctor called "tactlessness." He was so adept in the laboratory that he was soon hired by Dr Louis-Joseph Banderly, director of a dental institute on the Rue Poissonnière. Banderly was only twenty-six. He came from near Saint-Jean d'Acre in the Holy Land. His appearance intrigued Albert. Banderly smoked strange-smelling cigarettes and cut a dashing figure in his well-made frock coat.

"I have a little brother your age," he tells the boy. "He'll have a good education. I'm sending him to the Ecole Orientale in Auteuil." Albert wonders what they teach there and if you could sail a boat to an oriental place.

Banderly's institute is a second-floor apartment, converted into consulting rooms and a surgery, with an office for Madame Campredon the cashier. The dentist installs his new employee in a laboratory on the fifth floor, connected to the suite downstairs by a telephone line. He also hires Paul Cheney, fourteen. "You'll need an assistant to help you build all these teeth and bridges."

Banderly starts Albert on ten francs a week.

"That's not enough," protest his parents.

"The oriental's a miser," fumes the boy to save face. After a few months Banderly raises the wage to fifteen francs.

"He's paying me *twenty* francs a week. He doubled my salary," Albert beams. His parents, mirroring his happiness, beam back.

Since this announcement Albert Martin's face has been an anxious mask. Banderly's paying fifteen francs a week, but his parents are expecting twenty.

"Could you lend me five francs?" he asks. The dentist is inspecting the laboratory. It seems a telephone wire has been cut.

"Why not?" obliges Banderly. "Have you a new hobby besides photography?" The boy is silent. The dentist checks the line, noting a pair of scissors on the counter. He puffs his cigarette. Blowing a perfect ring, he conceals an urge to ask more questions. He cuts a wire to get me up here, then asks for extra money. Why? Banderly doesn't press. Albert sighs with relief.

After another week, "I need another five francs, Monsieur."

Banderly hesitates. "All right." Children and their secrets. "If he doesn't repay me, I'll dock his future salaries," he tells the cashier.

On 7 May, when Madame Campredon gives the boy his pay envelope, it contains only five francs. "Cheat! That filthy . . . !" Then Albert remembers how tactlessness cost him a previous job.

He runs to his parents. "Banderly paid me only five francs this week. His pockets are stuffed with gold. These foreigners are cunning. They don't appreciate good work. They pay us like Chinamen!"

"I'll speak to this dentist," Albert's father leaps up, forgetting the pear on his plate, "and demand your money."

"No! Papa!" Albert cries. His father showing up and shooting off his mouth! Banderly will tell him the truth!

* * *

Albert Martin is pedaling along the Rue de Montmartre. "Dirty Turk. The cashier put him up to it. These two pretend to be nice, but it's a charade. They're crooks trying to ruin me. When Carrara needed money he hit his bank messenger over the head with a carriage key!"

Madame Campredon is a young widow. When business is slow she sits sewing by the window, imagining herself mistress of Banderly's establishment. She and the young doctor bicycle every Sunday in the Bois de Boulogne. As they pedal side by side, she thinks of them as a couple. After their ride they lunch in Neuilly with her father, Monsieur Hardy, a retired legionnaire living on a small pension. Monsieur Hardy loves the perfect manners of Dr Banderly, not to mention his substantial income. "Soon, you'll be happily married," he tells his widowed girl.

Two days after paying Albert the paltry five francs, Madame Campredon notices the boys in the laboratory haven't left for the day. She telephones. "It's late. Finish up."

"Go Paul. I'm busy." Alone, Albert punctures the gas line.

"Those two always come down together," Madame Campredon thinks and rings again. "Time to go home, little one."

"Send up Dr Banderly. I smell gas."

Banderly leaves a patient to go and check. First he cuts the telephone as a joke. Now he's going to blow me up. Feeling uneasy, the doctor closes the pipe. "Someone will fix it tomorrow." Albert is staring at the floor.

"And how will you spend this lovely evening?" The dentist chooses small talk. He turns to roll a cigarette. His back faces Albert. The boy takes a heavy stamping hammer and hits him on the head, grabbing his frock coat to ease him to the floor. Then he hammers Banderly on the face and chest. The agonized dentist is in spasms, choking on blood. The boy can't look. He rifles his pockets. "Thirty-two francs, fifty! I thought he was rich!" Banderly is moving his head. Albert takes a folded handkerchief from the dentist's trousers. Pressing it firmly over the nose and gasping mouth, he stares out the window, listening to his own pounding heart as Banderly's slows to absolute stillness.

"The loot must be with his conspirator!" He takes a wrench and tip-toes to the second floor. Madame Campredon is a picture of calm absorption in an upholstered armchair, sewing a button on Banderly's shirt.

"Good. You've come down."

9 mai 1898 - 38 Rue Poissonnière. Assassinat du M. Banderly dentiste
par le M. Martin un Vue du Bureau où martin a tenté d'assassiner la Caissière

MURDER OF BANDERLY, BOULVARD POISSONIÈRE, 10. 5. 98
9 May 1898, 38 Rue Poissonnière, murder of Banderly, dentist, by Martin
View of the office where Martin tried to murder the cashier

Albert catches his breath. "May I please ... have a ... a piece of thread?"

"Of course, *mon petit.*" As she takes a spool from her work basket, he hits her with the wrench. She falls to her knees, rises, and staggers through the clinic. He follows, pounding her face and jaw. She's at the window. "Murderer! ... Help! ... Get help!" Passersby look up to see a woman blood-red.

"I'd better fly!" Albert bolts.

People in the street don't see a boy run from the building. They want to save the woman in the window. Panting from the climb, they meet her gruesome figure on the landing. "To the fifth floor. Something's ... happened to the doctor!" Her nose is pulp. She can hardly speak for spitting teeth.

The passersby race to the attic and force the laboratory door. Banderly's in a pool of blood. His pockets are inside out. Next to his head is a five-pound hammer and a cyclist's cap. They bring this to Madame Campredon. "It's Albert's!"

The cashier's face is purple. Abundant hemorrhaging has ruptured blood vessels under the skin into a painful inflammation. "The boy will find me! Take me to my father's!" But Monsieur Hardy's apartment is too small for her to be moved there. She is placed in a room at the dental institute. Thick curtains, pulled over the windows, protect her eyes and dampen the sound of the traffic outside. Practically smothered by bandages, she lies weeping on a couch draped with sheets. Her father attends her during the day, whispering endearments, feeding her bits of cooked fruit. A sister of charity sits by her at night, murmuring prayers on a rosary.

Bertillon arrives the next morning and goes directly to the corpse. He has trouble photographing in the tiny space. Sun flooding the laboratory obscures the detail. He blocks the window with a camera dark cloth, counting on flash to pick out the particulars. It explodes on the sideboard and doorway molding, but he's got the death cell clearly enough to disgust a jury.

Bertillon comes down to take a picture of the cashier's office. He can't concentrate. Madame Campredon in the next room is groaning. He wants to take another shot, but he's troubled by her wails. He should do something, pay his respects, perhaps. He carries his camera to her dim chamber. It smells of ether. A crack in the drapes throws light on the tiny, white mummy, sunk into the couch. He sets up his tripod, studies the cashier upside-down on the ground glass. But he can't take this picture.

Trying not to make the floor squeak, he approaches her, impatient and frightened, hoping not to bungle his visit by saying something inappropriate. Face to face, she's more than he can bear.

"Could you . . . help me?"

"But how Madame? I'm a photographer!" Grabbing his equipment, he escapes.

* * *

Albert Martin is wandering around Paris. Mud rubbed on his clothes hides Banderly's blood. He has bought a new cyclist's cap. He reads *Le Petit Journal* to study the reports of his crime. On the front page there's a line drawing of himself, smiling with his hands in his pockets. "I made that picture! Mama sold me with one of my own photographs!"

He buys a scarf to hide his face. The railroad stations are crawling with detectives. He takes a tram to the Buttes Chaumont, Noisy-le-Sec, and Bondy, eating once a day to make Banderly's money last. He registers in flop houses as "Benoît" or "Durand."

"I used to warn the doctor he carried too much money. He kept gold in his vest! He was proud. He worked hard to have his own clinic." Gauze muffles Madame Campredon's ravings. Cochefert is in her office inspecting the drawers. "We're combing the city. We have agents at all the railroad stations. They'll arrest the boy. We'll find out why he did this. We'll bring him to you, and you'll ask him yourself."

"Please, Monsieur Chief Inspector." Madame Campredon's doctor, overhearing the last phrase, takes him aside. "Seeing the boy will *kill* her." Humbled, Cochefert leaves the dentist's institute to look for Albert's friends.

"He wanted to go to America," says Balloche. "Check the wharfs. That's where you'll find him, buying women and eating lobster in fancy restaurants." The boy's fantasy makes Cochefert want to laugh.

Albert has written to his sister from Neuilly-sur-Seine. She gives Cochefert the letter. "Banderly said I cut the telephone wire and the gas line. It isn't true. He threatened me. He boxed my ears. I saw red." Cochefert sighs. "When you get this I'll have drowned."

He isn't going to kill himself, thinks Cochefert. Death to these children is a fairytale.

Albert Martin is out of money and hungry. He returns to the Rue de Navarin. A butcher on the Rue Breda sees him pass with a cap over his eyes. "Run! Your picture's in the paper. Detectives are waiting at your parents'!" Albert ignores the pantomime. He goes to Balloche, a locksmith on his street. "His son will take me in. We're friends for life."

"You're crazy coming here," says young Balloche, practically fainting at the sight of the fugitive. "They're waiting for you."

"I'm going to drown myself. I have to tell mother good-bye. Keep me here and send for her."

"We can't take you in! They'll arrest us too!"

"Coward! I'll go to the color merchant! He'll find mama. If he tells her I'm headed for the Seine, she'll come." The color merchant shakes his head. Albert tries every shopkeeper on the street. All refuse to help him.

"I have to go home!" He ducks into his building which is swarming with Cochefert's agents. The boy drops to his stomach and crawls toward the door to the cellar. A neighbor sees him. "Madame Martin! Your son is in the basement!" The agents run down, but he takes another stair to the fifth floor.

Before stepping into the light he knocks on another door.

"Leave Albert. We can't help you!"

"I'll fly off the roof."

"Come down, my child!" His mother is in the hallway. She hears banging doors in the attic. Agents push her into her apartment. "Please! He'll jump!"

They run upstairs.

"Call the chief. He's ours."

Ordered to stay behind closed doors, the Martins sit in miserable silence, listening to their son being brought down in chains. Suddenly Madame Martin flings open the door. Albert is grey and shrunken on the landing. Seeing her he loses his footing.

"Wretched boy! Wretched boy!" She throws herself on the wasted child.

"Mama!" he wails, trying to swallow. "Why did you tell me to come down?"

"I was afraid you'd jump."

"You delivered me, mama!"

* * *

Cochefert's seen plenty of children like Albert. Here's a poor, sick boy who craved ordinary pleasures, studied his dreary parents, and decided his salary would save them from some imagined misery. What did he do but fail to make good on a lie? How many serious juvenile crimes are inspired by similar agonies?

Cochefert knows every kind of killer. None are born evil. They're twisted by poor education and bad examples. Little Paul Cheney, Albert's colleague, told Cochefert that all Albert talked about as they built teeth was Carrara. Cochefert wonders why criminal contagion isn't discussed at the trial.

After Albert Martin's trial Cochefert tells Henri Massonneau, a journalist writing a book on capital punishment, what he thinks about children who kill: "If I had the power to decide their futures I wouldn't execute them or even sentence them to forced labor. I'd build great asylums in the country with gardens and shady trees. Soft breezes and the perfumes of rose gardens would comfort these boys. I'd build gaming rooms. Cards, billiards, chess, tennis, and boxing would teach them fair play.

"If I had time I'd take them, one by one, and teach them. I'd make them talk about what they love. I'd ease them out of their pain. I'd do sleight-of-hand magic and make them laugh. I'd give them cameras so they could photograph their comrades, their guardians, the landscape, anything that caught their eye. In our system the eye of the camera convicts them. I'd use it to heal the madness of these pitiful children."

"You won't mind if I devote a chapter to you and include this charming utopia?"

"I'm bound to be misunderstood."

"You're an arm of the law, but you're also a man of compassion, a father who loves children and will do anything to restore their innocence."

"My idealism is impossible. The jury takes one look at the photographs, the body, the blood, the horrible room . . ."

13 Yellow Jack

2 June 1898, 119 Rue Saint-Denis,
1ˢᵗ Arrondissement, Marie-Oliva Leprince, 50,
maker and wholesaler of artificial flowers
and feathers, strangled by Xavier Schneider, 21,
her delivery boy. Condemned to death.
Sentence commuted to forced labor for life.

She didn't like being pinched into whalebone. She wore loose gowns like certain English ladies do. I've seen this in Paris among women who collect exotic curios, palm trees, tiger skins, and the like. She didn't need those things. Her petite elegance was enough.

Besides, she had the sweetest temper you could imagine. There wasn't a day I didn't thank heaven for having married her. She was a good mother, too. Her health was fragile, so we had to stop after one child. Our son is an artilleryman in Douai, a boy with common sense who takes after me. Oliva made a cult of beauty. She was our angel.

We earned our living with artificial flowers which we fabricated from silks and feathers. She trained herself by pressing real flowers and collecting books of botanical engravings which she traced sitting up in bed while I slept. She knew feathers. She chose the best iridescent peacock plumes and rare displays of snowy egret which milliners assemble following today's fashions. Their hats would have been vulgar piles without the pieces my wife provided.

We did well because we cut our expenses to the bone. Our space was a cheerless warehouse, but she turned it into a comfortable home. She put up wallpapers and hung paintings without the frames. She hated the confused, overstuffed styles that people in our quarter hang on to. They stick to the old ways, she said, because they don't know any better.

She liked the modern look, which we couldn't afford, so she found old commercial pieces with simple lines and polished them up. In this dusty building our place smelled like lemons and vetiver. It was the scent of feminine virtue. She added a few mirrors and put a vitrine over the bronze clock in our bedroom. She waxed the floors and kept them bare. Now my darling wife is dead. Without her I'm as good as dead too.

I can't remember which arrest it was, but at the time I wore my hair in a page-boy. Bertillon, a sour bird, measured me and noted on my card that I was exceptionally tall. Why did he need numbers to decide that? Then he made me sit in front of his camera. I was on file. I had no beard or mustache. The old gentleman photographed a medieval prince.

We were such good managers we didn't even keep a regular servant. Last February when we hired the boy to make deliveries, it was strictly temporary. It was the busy season. The milliners and dressmakers were preparing their spring lines, and there was a big demand for our supplies. We needed help badly. He said he was Albert Protat, twenty-five. I'd hoped to find someone younger since we could only pay him three francs a day.

I'm really Xavier Schneider, twenty-one. I gave these people the name and age on some papers I stole from a cabby I roomed with. He was the real Albert Protat. He went to the country one weekend. I broke into his trunk. A locked trunk is begging to be

MURDER OF MADAME LEPRINCE, 119 RUE SAINT-DENIS, 3. 6. 98

Murder of Madame Leprince: view of the bedroom

opened. I was desperate for a job. I had a record with the police. I couldn't say who I really was. The real Protat wouldn't have cared. He already had work. I knew I'd never see him again. I stole his identity. It was temporary, a short stop on a longer journey.

He was weak and hungry, a lost soul, living on thin air. I figured he'd work for hardly anything. Me and my stupid penny pinching. I should have known something was wrong when I first saw him. He looked like he'd been starving himself and towered over me like Lazarus stepped from the grave.

There was something wrong with his spine. His hips were out of joint. His legs dangled like a skeleton's when he walked. I didn't think this meant he was dangerous. Something evil was written all over him. I just didn't know how to read the signs. My wife didn't say a word, though I know she judged everything by appearances. I never let someone's looks influence me, even if they are alarming. Maybe he had a disease. I don't know what it was. I wasn't going to embarrass him by pointing out his infirmities.

They say your looks are your destiny. Mine frighten people. I'm not ashamed. They're part of my lineage, my history. People in my family look the same way. My grandmother is quite mad, and we have some nutty relatives in Alsace on my father's side we call the *fous* Schneider. I steal because I hate to work. It's how I need to live, but I've worked when I had to. A string of jobs I can brag about. I helped out at a hairdresser's, was a porter at the central markets, drove a delivery carriage. I was a rag-and-bone man and even stooped to selling shoe polish on the street. My favorite job was as an extra at the Châtelet Theater.

His hands were long and spidery. My wife couldn't take her eyes off them when he helped her box the flowers. "They're so alive, so expressive, they dance," she said. She noticed his fingers were all the same length, and the thumb of his right hand stretched beyond his index finger. Aren't a person's hands supposed to be a clue to his character? If they were, I didn't know what the boy's hands meant, what powers they might conceal. I wonder what Oliva thought they expressed. Impulsiveness? A restless spirit? Cunning? Moral deficiency? I should have realized these hands were going to destroy everything I cared about.

> I scare myself because half the time I don't know what I'm doing. My mother calls me the family curse. I've stolen so much money from her over the years, I can't blame her for thinking I'm insane. The way I act is ruining her, but I suppose I have her to thank for keeping most of my crimes a secret. Maybe she's to blame for what I've become. Since my father died I've provided for all my own needs. I've always liked my drink, which makes me uglier than I already am. I take wine for courage, but absinthe, a modern drink, stimulates my creativity. Unfortunately, it gives me fits. At fifteen during a seizure I went haywire and started shooting a revolver into the Boulevard Saint-Martin. I drink to forget my troubles. I get so depressed all I can think of is suicide. So far it's only a fantasy.

He showed up every morning at seven-thirty. Since he did the jobs we wanted we were satisfied. At midday he always took lunch with us. It was pathetic to see him gulp down three or four helpings and scrape the serving dishes for what was left. With all he put away he stayed pitifully thin.

> My greatest fear is not having enough to eat. I began my criminal career stealing food. That was before my father died. At thirteen the police nabbed me for stealing a bottle of milk. It was always easier to steal what I needed than ask my parents. I hated to risk

being refused. I stuffed myself at the Leprinces' table. They didn't seem to mind.

My boss's wife was a princess. We always joked when we worked together. We were very similar. She was imaginative and curious. Style was everything to her. She had great chic and was fascinated with the world. She got it all out of her books. Her fawning husband never took her anywhere. She was his slave in the studio. I have the theater to console me and the mysterious dreams that float through my brain after a few glasses of absinthe.

As a hobby she collected butterflies and scarab beetles which she arranged in concentric circles in big frames. One of these hangs in the studio next to the window where she had her work table. She said mounting insects in all the colors of the rainbow trained her powers of discernment. I think she liked daydreaming with these curiosities, getting lost in their strange forms.

I used to overhear her and the boy cheerfully conversing. She told me the outer edge of his ear looked like a shell she might have found on the beach. With his monkey hands and crooked spine, I suppose he became another of her exotic specimens. "Our new boy is the color of a quince!" she'd laugh. He was. Though I wouldn't have put it that way. She had the artist's eye. He was such a contrast to her delicate charm and love of beauty that for the short time he was with us he became our benevolent beast.

She had her feathers, bugs, and flowers, but I'd been places. I had seduced English girls who still write to me. I wanted to tell her about them, about all I learned in my travels. I wanted to tell her that to straighten me out my mother had me sent to a correctional facility in North Africa where I caught the fevers which permanently sapped my strength. I wanted to tell her I was so miserable in a penitentiary in Tunisia I tried to asphyxiate myself with carbon monoxide. Had she noticed the slight paralysis in my arm from that attempt? I wanted to tell her about being sick as a child, which made me too feeble to work, about my father dying from complications in his chest when I was fifteen, how I get drunk, and sick, and morose, and want to kill myself. After a time I might have. But I had places to go. It was too late for confidences.

We've never left France, but our hired boy spoke Arabic and Italian. He could even make himself understood in English. His French was oddly flamboyant. He twisted the meanings of words so you thought you were reading a novel of kings and queens. "Thank you for giving me such a prominent place at your hearth," he'd say to tell us he felt at home. "I have my decorum to protect," he'd complain about his miserable salary. "My scabrous insouciance is entirely of my own devising," he'd apologize after making a mistake with an order. He told Oliva he'd acted in the theater, another mystery we never bothered to investigate.

With looks like mine I always thought I was destined for the stage. I have something in common with Paganini, greatest virtuoso of all time. A monstrous talent in his fingers. He was more than a violinist. He was a skeleton, oozing with magnetism. I wouldn't have known about him except for bumping into his photograph in a bookstall on the quays. I thought I was looking at myself. He was tall and dark. Glossy hair fell over his shoulders. His hands wrapped around his instrument like a hydra. I had to have that picture. I came back, again and again, till the bookseller started to squirm. When he was busy with a customer, I slipped Paganini into my pocket. I carried him with me like my own personal visiting card. We're both visitors from worlds beyond this one. He was possessed by the devil when he played. He would have been a criminal if it weren't for music, if he hadn't

175

MURDER OF MADAME LEPRINCE, 119 RUE SAINT-DENIS, 3. 6. 98
Murder of Madame Leprince: view of the room used as the shop

been able to drive his audiences into a frenzy. Maybe he was ill. I know he died young. That was before my time, but I recognized a soul mate.

My neighbors were smarter than me about our new delivery boy. They found him revolting and told me so. Hiring him, I'd infected their workplace. I thought they were crazy. Some people see the world so clearly. They act on a general impression. I should have listened to their common sense. They were afraid to meet him on the stairs. He might talk to them. What would they say back? I was influenced by my wife who found the boy novel and intriguing.

She became oddly attached to him. So did I, though now I wonder why, with his fancy phrases and the frightening shadow he cast in the hallways. Perhaps it was because he seemed unusually intelligent. He was about the age of our son. I missed having someone to advise. I told him I'd find him another job after we let him go. He seemed pleased. I like to think he looked to me as a son does a father. Now it's too late. It's all my fault for not protecting her.

The year my father died I grabbed 300 francs from my mother. After prison for that little caper, to show her I'd repented I found a job with some merchants on the Rue du Cloître Saint-Merrie. I saw where they kept their money and was back to stealing. The 1,500 francs I got took me to Switzerland and Italy, where I learned Italian. But the police found me and locked me up. As soon as I was free I stole 6,000 more francs from my mother. I suppose I should feel guilty. She was just a greengrocer and had saved the money for years, a centime at a time. I needed it to play the horses.

The Leprinces knew I didn't like getting three francs a day, but I had my reasons for staying on. I wanted the money they were piling up in their secretary. It was early June. I knew my time with them was coming to an end.

He did what we asked. I didn't worry about his knowing where we kept our savings. The secretary was in full view from the studio. Once I saw him watching me put 150 francs into a drawer, but I didn't worry. We never reproached him or criticized him for nosing around, for anything, really. We got used to him.

I cut costs by making my own deliveries outside of Paris. Last Thursday morning I was scheduled to go to Meaux at nine. I asked him to come with me to the Gare de l'Est to help buy my ticket and check in the bags of samples. I told him to go back to the apartment and deliver some orders to florists in town between eleven and twelve.

After I put my boss on the train I filled a rush order like he asked. I had a few creative absinthes before returning to the apartment. I was drifting. My feet hardly touched the ground. The building was practically empty. All the brokers had gone home to eat. I still had the strap I'd used to hold my boxes together. She always ate around eleven-thirty. She was in the dining room. Her meal was on the table. She shouldn't have been there. She got in my way. I tied my strap with a sliding knot and surprised her from behind. She had the neck of a child. My hands were more of a weapon than I imagined. To be sure I'd done the job, I hurled my strap smartly and tightened it around the key ring at the end. A perfect fit. I'm a virtuoso. I dragged her body to the studio. She'd been making roses. I placed it under the window near her flowers and butterflies.

I took her scissors from the work table and broke into the secretary. I got 700 francs in notes and 300 in change. I took some bonds and real-estate shares. What was I was going to do with them? When I threw the drawer of the secretary into a cupboard I found her watch, a pretty antique. I kept it to give to one of the English girls whose letters I keep in my room. I also took her marriage contract. With it was a photograph of her when she was young. I put it in my pocket next to Paganini.

MURDER OF MADAME LEPRINCE, 119 RUE SAINT-DENIS, 3. 6. 98

2 June 1898, 119 Rue Saint-Denis, murder of Madame Leprince, broker in artificial flowers,
by Schneider, Xavier, her employee: discovery of the body

He was supposed to meet me at the Gare de l'Est to help carry my bags. When I got to the station at four-thirty, he wasn't there. I waited and took a cab home. The place was unusually still. I called, but no one answered. I found her in the studio, lying on the floor next to the counter. She had a far-away look, as if she were listening to music. Light poured in from the window. The scene would have been enchanting if my poor wife weren't there dead.

My heart was pounding. I was too shocked to cry out or weep. All I could think was that our monster must have killed her. I went for the police. They showed me a photograph of our delivery boy from one of his previous arrests. They published it in the newspapers and gave it to detectives who patrol the railway stations. It shows him with long hair. He had short hair when he worked for us. Nobody's going to recognize him.

Afterwards, I was hungry as a horse. I had a good lunch in a brasserie, changed clothes, and went to the Gare de l'Est, thinking I'd take the train to Epernay. I realized my boss might be returning from Meaux on the same line. So I jumped off and made my way across the border to Strasbourg. I bought a pistol. A solid weapon made me more comfortable. I didn't know what I was going to do with it. Anything seemed possible. Then I took a train south to Mulhouse.

I noticed a traveling company was doing a production of *Madame Sans-Gêne* at the Municipal Theater. I counted on Sardou to cheer me up. A sleight-of-hand plot about a laundress married to one of Napoléon I's generals.

When the Emperor threatened to strangle an actor with the cord on his uniform I got so excited I grabbed my pistol and shot it into the air. Everyone in the theater, even the players, realized *my* drama was the one to watch. Some devil cops tried to grab me. Sinister bastards. I ran to the foyer and emptied my revolver. One bullet hit a sergeant. Later I learned it only grazed the handcuffs in his pocket. I reserved the last bullet for myself. As the fiends closed in, I put the gun to my temple. Blood all over my face! I was so confused I confessed.

I loved her tiny hands straightening my collar. She couldn't stop arranging things. All she touched became something worth admiring. She cut silk into any flower you could name. Her lilies were white and waxy. Her parrot tulips burst into flames. Her roses, tinged with mauve and pale yellow, were edged with magenta. No two looked alike. This dismayed the other brokers, but it inspired the milliners and dressmakers. Her work was so full of knowledge and passion. She even crimped a piece of silk for a lampshade in our bedroom to remind me of moss roses in late summer. As she lay dead in the studio, serenely, with light streaming through the window, her tongue between her teeth was a tiny rosebud.

I'm a mystery. Nobody knows what I'm made of. They only see a freak. The bullet I gave myself was a clue for them to look inside me. That's why I got X-rayed, so they could see into my brain, my very core. They sat me down and made me hold my breath while a lot of explosions went off.

At the trial I saw the picture of my skull and a grey shadow that represents my imagination. The bullet was a little white arrow behind my right ear. The jury sentenced me to death in thirty-five minutes. My lawyer, Henri Robert, used the bullet in my head to argue I was deranged. It saved me from the scaffold.

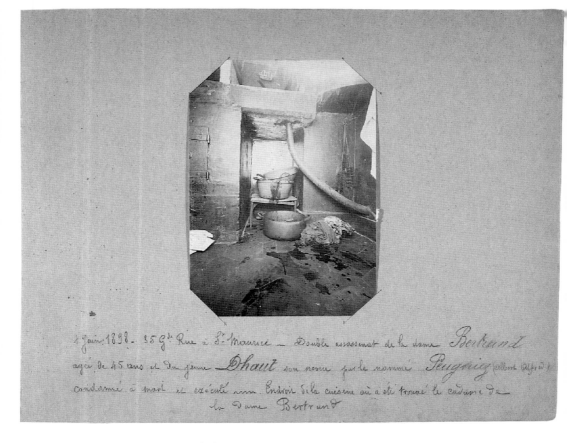

4 JUNE 1898, 35 GRANDE RUE IN SAINT-MAURICE

Double murder of Madame Bertrand, age 45, and young Dhaut, her nephew, by Peugniez
(Albert–Alfred) sentenced to death and executed: corner of the kitchen where the body
of Madame Bertrand was found

14 Captured

4 June 1898, 35 Grande Rue, Saint-Maurice,
southeast of Paris, Nicolas-Eugénie Bertrand, 45,
laundress, and her nephew Octave-Victor Dhaut,
7, schoolboy, murdered with a hammer and
razor by Albert-Alfred Peugniez, 21, roofer's
apprentice, thief. Sentenced to death
14 December 1898. Guillotined 1 February 1899.

Bertillon shoots the dining room where Albert Peugniez drank wine and beer with his hosts in Saint-Maurice, a country village near a great wood. He includes the stuffed deer's head, straw hat and leather satchel, the cape on a hook. Flash exposes the kitchen beyond, shelves with soup tureens, an ironstone teapot, pitchers, soup plates, a morning coffee bowl, bottles of wine or olive oil, a laboratory of daily life.

To show Madame Bertrand under the sink, he lowers the tripod to floor level, using a wide-angle lens to scan the tight space. The lens makes strange choices, shrinking the woman's head, magnifying her apron, jacket, and kitchen towels into a coarsely woven landscape. A chair looks less like furniture than architecture. Common objects become contorted emblems of unspeakable acts. He opens the lens for ten minutes, during which he explodes flash against the wall of the sink to ensure a clear reading of the victim's head and gaping throat. The angle catches her profile in a linear halo made by the rim of a bowl. The center of the shot is not this rondel but Madame Bertrand's hand, useless against that of her attacker, yet in death, a massive exaggeration.

In another kitchen view, the camera scans oil lamps, coffee pots, candle sticks, a ladle, trivet, a coffee grinder, the stove, the sink with Madame Bertrand barely visible beneath it. These homely tools are a mere backdrop for a foreground of more important things. The napkin Madame Bertrand was pressing when Peugniez crept behind her still lies on the ironing board which extends across a table. On its pristine cloth, the hammer and razor look like surgical instruments. Did Peugniez put them there and leave or did the police arrange them for Bertillon to record? Next to the victim's pile of perfect linens they are a still life asserting Peugniez's dominant authority. The arrangement includes a popular print which shows a mounted Roman soldier overpowering a woman with hair flying, arms raised in protest.

In Bertillon's selective lens the corners of the images darken into shadow, transforming a common kitchen, curiously, into a planetary sphere, whose forces twist the relations between things. The photographer finds himself decoding an agonized contest between the boy and his victim. The pictures are strange. They're unlike any he's ever made.

In the bedroom, he uses another strategy, treating the space as a theatrical stage box. He records the child's blood on the marble fireplace, floor, and the mechanical horse. The adjoining cabinet with little Octave bludgeoned in his bed is too small and dark to make a reasonable picture. He wheels the crib to the bedroom, hangs a light-colored blanket over the armoire to catch the flash, and sets the camera away from the tableau to include the floor Peugniez had come to wax and repair.

In one of these tableaux the door to the bedroom is closed. In the other with the door open, Bertillon can feel Peugniez entering with his hammer. Cochefert and his agents are searching Paris and the suburbs, coming up with nothing. Bertillon, scanning doors, beds and tables, fancies he's captured the killer.

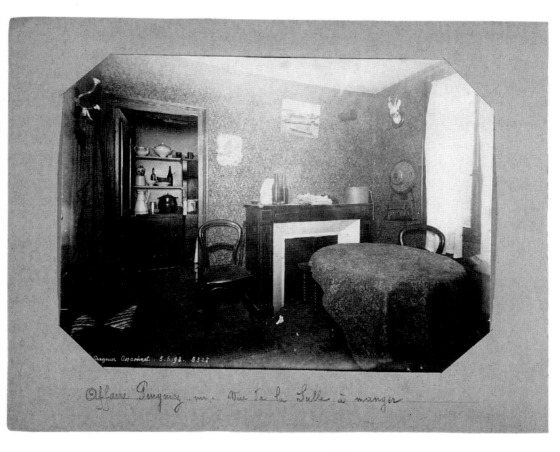

Affaire Peugniez ... Vue de la Salle à manger

PEUGNIEZ MURDER, 5. 6. 98

Peugniez affair: view of the dining room

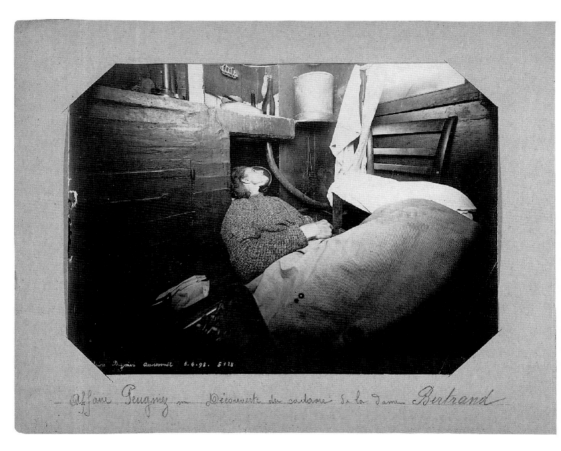

PEUGNIEZ MURDER, 5. 6. 98

Peugniez affair: discovery of the body of Madame Bertrand

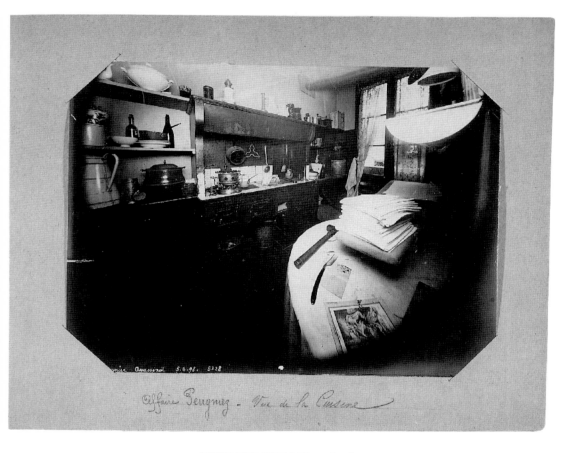

PEUGNIEZ MURDER, 5. 6. 98

Peugniez affair: view of the kitchen

PEUGNIEZ MURDER, 5. 6. 98

Peugniez affair: discovery of the body of young Dhaut in his bed

Affaire Peugniez.... *Vue de la Chambre à coucher avec le cheval mécanique ensanglanté de l'enfant*

PEUGNIEZ MURDER, 5. 6. 98

Peugniez affair: view of the bedroom with the child's blood on the mechanical horse

15 Deity

14 April 1899, suitcase containing the headless torso of a 20- to 30-year-old woman with arms pulled from the Seine near the Pont de Sèvres, Boulogne-sur-Seine. Circumstances of the crime and identity of the victim never satisfactorily determined.

Alive, she must have been powerful because in death she looked nothing short of majestic. Her bearing was a warrior's. There was no stiffening. Her arms and hands looked supple and strong. Even headless she seemed to speak: "I'm a holy terror. A modern sacrifice. Know me."

Her siren's call beckoned Bertillon. Framed on the ground glass of his camera she became an ancient breastplate, a perfect architectural fragment. Bertillon stared so long, the nipples, navel, and sex turned into a mask, another camera eye mirroring his bewilderment, glaring back at him.

* * *

The murderer put the freshly sectioned torso into a suitcase, first wrapping it in rags so it wouldn't leak blood and betray his ghastly deed. He must have waited till late afternoon — in mid-April it was stormy and dark — before he carted the case to the Seine where he threw it from a bridge.

The floating suitcase wasn't long in the river. Forty yards from the Pont de Sèvres, three dock workers on a barge saw something like a box in the waves. One jumped in a dingy for a better look. That's when he realized it was a valise, bulging and stone-heavy. He broke a handle getting it out.

These boatmen brought their find to the quay. They unbuckled the straps and started screaming. A woman brutally butchered. Clots on her neck and pelvis. Stinking of putrefaction. They called the police.

* * *

The medical examiners asked her practical questions. Who were you in life? How did you die? They had a legal right. Their job was to show whoever performed the atrocity would soon be under judicial control. Like Bertillon, they gave her remains absolute authority. A killer would emerge from their scrupulous examinations, or so they believed. Their knowledge turned out to be insufficient, but it was all they had.

They decided she had been dead a couple of days before she was dismembered. They analyzed the clavicles to establish her age. She was around twenty-five. Even without a corset her small breasts and waist seemed almost stylish. Her skin was smooth and very white. Her hair, judging from a few strands at the nape of the neck, had been a warm chestnut-brown.

She was not a prostitute, alcoholic, or vagrant. Her solid constitution showed vibrant health and a good appetite. She'd made love and born offspring. Examining her belly they found she'd had a child a few months before her death.

She'd been a seamstress. The large, capable hands weren't those of the usual needleworker. Deep holes in her fingers meant she'd sewn resistant materials, shoe leather or other coarse goods. Besides these stigmata her hands were clean, without calluses, the nails well cared for.

Dr Socquet autopsied the heart and lungs looking for clots and congestion caused by a bullet to the head, a blade to the throat, or a rope around the neck. What reduced her to something to cut up?

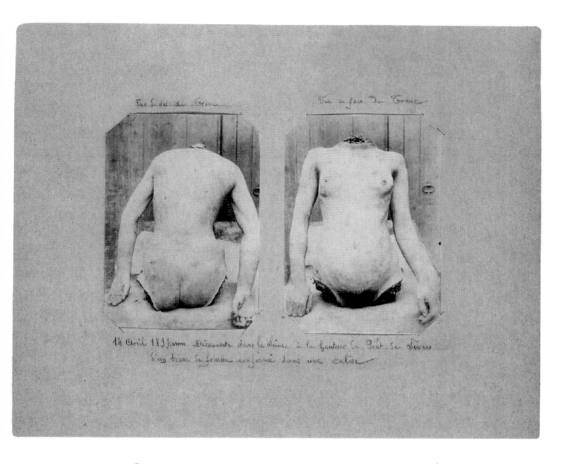

14 APRIL 1899, DISCOVERY IN THE SEINE, NEAR THE PONT DE SÈVRES,
OF A WOMAN'S TORSO CONCEALED IN A SUITCASE

View of the back of the torso; view of the front of the torso

He couldn't tell. He studied the contents of the stomach but learned nothing except that she'd eaten two hours before she died.

The sections of the legs were rather clean. They followed the groove of each thigh when disjoined from the femur. Socquet said it's difficult to detach the head of the femur from the pelvic cavity housing it. The tendon has to be cut precisely. He found the operation rather crude. This was also true of the cut to the neck between the first dorsal and last cervical vertebrae. Who was the killer? Not a professional butcher. That's all Socquet could conclude. He removed parts of the cadaver to examine under a microscope. Maybe there he'd find a motive for the crime. He found nothing others hadn't seen simply by looking at her.

The suitcase got the same attention. Bertillon photographed it, like the torso, in daylight without flash. It was made of brown cloth, attached to a wooden frame by copper rivets. The interior was lined with heavy blue-and-grey-striped ticking. It was in good condition but not new. The metal bars of the buckles had left brown traces on the straps. The torso was too big. It had to be forced inside, making it impossible for the murderer to pull the straps tight or use the little lock between the handles. With so many gaps, it was surprising the thing hadn't taken on water and gotten sucked into the undertow.

This particular suitcase was Parisian, manufactured in large quantities by a Monsieur Bernheim on the Rue Abel-Rabaud. It was the exclusive model of his establishment and cost sixteen francs, fifty centimes. Bernheim sells his bags to a bazaar on the Rue de Rivoli that distributes them throughout the city. Two weeks ago the bazaar, clearing out the line, sold this model for the last time. Would a clerk there or in any of the outlets remember who bought it?

The rags that wrapped the remains were also scrutinized. They amounted to three pieces of a man's calico shirt with the initials AP hastily stitched in red cotton under the pocket by a laundress. Another pattern of thread on the shirt was less common. Called a *fil Breton* it looked like a ribbon in a boutonnière. Laundresses add this when

Découverte d'un tronc de femme en Seine

Aspect de la Valise renfermant le
tronc de femme

DISCOVERY OF A WOMAN'S TORSO IN THE SEINE

View of the suitcase that held the torso of the woman

clients have the same initials. The collar had a number 38 in blue, with an X over it. These are makers' inscriptions, indicating collar size and series of fabrication. The cuffs were attached with porcelain buttons. There was also a white handkerchief, with no identification, and part of a woman's white cotton shift, trimmed with a crocheted scallop and held together by a safety pin.

The suitcase and linen were washed and dried so they could be displayed in the public viewing room of the morgue. Police agents interviewed more than 200 laundresses around Boulogne and Sèvres who provided lists of their clients' names and laundry marks. Many people examined these rags. The laundresses were confident their marks would solve the crime.

* * *

Cochefert ordered fishermen and barge workers to drag the Seine with boat hooks. The people of Boulogne and nearby villages were so fascinated by the morbid discovery they spent all day on the Pont de Sèvres watching the draggers.

Agents interviewed the citizens of Ville d'Avray, Chaville, Viroflay, and the faubourgs around Sèvres and Versailles. They searched the railroad and omnibus stations, the tramways, and the toll houses on the Pont de Sèvres. Had anyone seen a person carrying a brown suitcase?

They searched the river's edge. It was muddy, tracked by rain. On the Grand-Rue in Sèvres, leading to Bellevue, they found drops of blood not washed away by the storms. Some were the size of five-franc pieces. This blood stopped at the entrance to Chaville. Whoever transported the suitcase, probably in a cart, got out there and went to the Seine on foot. How did he walk for miles carrying a corpse?

Madame Renaudin at 12 Grande-Rue in Chaville claimed she'd seen an individual wearing a blue worker's blouse, carrying two heavy suitcases. She said he stopped to rest every fifty yards. One suitcase was striped. The other was like that found in the Seine.

In front of the railroad station at the Pont de Sèvres agents found more blood in a large pool. Drops followed the left curb of the bridge and stopped at a gas lamp on the Boulogne side. On the day of the crime the toll-house for the Sèvres side of the bridge closed early, so its lamps were out. The toll-house for Boulogne, open all night, gave off a lurid light.

The trails of blood doubled in the middle of the bridge. This meant the murderer, spotlighted by the Boulogne toll-house, retraced his steps to get to the Sèvres side where he could hide in the shadows and drop his cargo.

Was this blood human? Blood on the street is common, especially in carriage traffic. Drivers are always cutting their hands, but just as often their horses get hurt and bleed. More blood found on the Issy road turned out to be an injured dog's.

Police agents questioned all the occupants of houses, hotels, and hospitals in the area about missing women. Chief detective Cochefert had a pile of letters on his desk from citizens describing lost loved ones. A Madame T., working in an administrative job, had recently disappeared. She was tall, brown-haired, and mother of a small child, which all corresponded to the victim in the suitcase.

Two other women were missing: Blanche Cadiot from outside Versailles, and Jeanne Rivière, a maid who registered at a placement office there. Before their stories could be followed they turned up. Four other women who disappeared from Sèvres several months ago were also found alive.

A couple of days before the torso was found a Monsieur G. noticed someone of thirty-five or forty on the Rue Saint-Merrie in Paris. He carried a brown suitcase in his right hand. Under his left arm was a round package the size of a human head. Passing the Rue Brisemiche he threw the package into a sewer where it disappeared after he pushed it down with his foot.

From a café facing the Sèvres police commissariat, the comings and goings of the authorities are in full view. The day the suitcase was found a man of thirty or thirty-five, medium build, a little stooped, and dressed like a worker in his Sunday best, entered the café and said, "Ah! Ah! . . . There's a woman cut in pieces . . ." Every time he sipped his drink he burst out laughing. He stayed three hours, watching the police station. From time to time, he asked the patron: "Eh well, no newspapers yet?" He appeared nervous, eyeing the groups in the streets. Then he left, never to return. He was unknown in the neighborhood, but his agitation was obvious.

The information was vast, chaotic, and contradictory. There were lists of false victims, *pseudo-assassinés,* claimed by their families as missing persons. Cochefert would have needed months to investigate them all. Needless to say, he didn't bother.

Straw among the rags in the suitcase gave rise to the idea that the crime might have occurred on a farm. It wasn't committed in central Paris, or why bring the corpse all the way west to the Pont de Sèvres? Only a river worker would throw a body in the water and cut it up to make it unrecognizable, in case it was fished out. But someone living and working on a barge wouldn't have had the privacy to kill, much less carve up his victim. The interior partitions of these boats are thin as paper.

Five days after the discovery, there was nothing new. At the Pont de Sèvres Cochefert threw a suitcase into the river. Inside he'd put a dismembered sheep. He wanted to see how many hours it would float. It sank in a bloody whirlpool. To the laughing journalists present he explained that the weather, wind, and atmosphere had changed since the day of the crime. What could they do but believe him?

A suicide was discovered in La Nièvre with linen marked AP. Was this the killer, driven to desperation? Cochefert decided it wasn't. Then someone found what he insisted were the legs of a woman. Cochefert identified them as the legs of a lamb. Monsieur Grosscuvre, a locksmith from Viroflay, noticed a battered suitcase in front of his shop. Suspecting a joke, he opened it to find a bottle containing a small coil of paper on which was written: "The Head."

This *cancan* went on for weeks until the authorities got tired, and the case was abandoned. No one ever penetrated the life and death of the woman who became a grisly torso. Or discovered the identity of her assassin. He is probably still walking the streets, paying his rent, paring his fingernails.

16 Ground Bird

9 May 1900, 4 Rue de Lutèce,
Colombes-dans-les-Champs, northwest of
Paris, Caroline-Céleste Fourmentin, 79,
former dressmaker, prostitute, vagrant,
raped, strangled, and eviscerated in the tool
shed where she lived. Murderer unknown.

Caroline-Céleste Fourmentin haunted the northwest suburbs of
Paris near Argenteuil and the race track at Colombes like a great
old heron. Thrown out of several rooming houses in Courbevoie and
La Garenne-Bezons as a nuisance, she slept under bridges, in public
gardens, in the plaster kilns of Ménilmontant and the basements of
building sites. Or she joined other vagabonds on the lawns of the
Champs de Mars, lying with heads touching and feet fanned in a pin-
wheel, for safety.

By the age of seventy she was too tired to be a nomad. Crossing
a field outside Colombes, she discovered an abandoned shed. She put
rags in the windows and hung a shredded carpet over the threshold,
adding a discarded stove, broken cot, and crockery from the dump.
Others who had the shanty before her left clothing which she used to
seal the walls against the cold. A shovel was her weapon of defense.
Nobody could get rid of her.

The mayor of Colombes decided she was demented and urged
her to enter a hospital. She refused. He sent an agent to order her

out. She barred the door, crying with the fury that carried her through the riots of 1848, 1851, and the Franco-Prussian War: "Evict me? Get a *proper* summons from the bailiff!" Humbled, he left. No one bothered her again. After a decade in Colombes, she was an indisputable fact.

Caroline-Céleste Fourmentin, born 6 December 1821, had been a dressmaker. Nearly eighty, she carried herself like a girl of eighteen. Her stride ate up the space around her. She was notorious among the authorities for a life of "irregularities": at twenty-eight, she got six months for theft; at fifty-seven, two months for organizing an unauthorized lottery; at sixty, two weeks for the same offence. Perhaps she'd been married; her only jewelry was a copper wedding ring. Her shriveled face, with white hair flying in all directions, and the loathsome rags on her long dry frame gave her the allure of a creature from a fairy tale.

Children who played near Caroline's shanty thought her flapping carpets spelled the hut of a witch. It seemed enchanted in early spring when the field was drenched with scents of lilac and cherry blossoms. Breezes downwind caught smells of neglect and the pungent odor of scorched casseroles. The children imagined this was the flesh and bones of luckless wanderers who got too close, whom "Aunt" Caroline clubbed with her shovel, burned alive, and ate. They dreamed at night of her gasping fetid breath.

In the safety of sunshine, they taunted, "Come out, Auntie! You old witch!" And they'd scamper off, half-hoping she'd catch them so they could tell stories of near-death from the crone with a hairy chin. They sneaked by her house, throwing stones through the carpets. A beak poked out. "I'll catch you! Gobble you up! Spit you to the winds!" And she'd chase them with her shovel, flinging it at their legs as they ran, screaming, slipping on the wet grass.

Their parents, attributing a quality of majestic solitude to old Caroline, referred to her as the "Mother of the Plain," by which they meant to lend dignity to her pathetic state. She accepted the phrase

9 MARCH 1900, RUE DE LUTÈCE IN COLOMBES-DANS-LES-CHAMPS

Murder of Fourmentin, Caroline-Céleste, age 79

View of the shed where the body was found

with feigned humility when accompanied by a few francs, secretly finding the patronage absurd.

At night the candle from Caroline's shed attracted other visitors: lost souls begged from her who had nothing. She gave them wine, and newspapers to fill the holes in their shoes. Strangers might be dangerous, but she craved the company and detained them with stories. With nowhere better to go, they stayed to listen as her ragged profile haunted the candlelight like a shadow play.

"I used to be a dressmaker." She leaned forward, elbows on her knees. "They called us *grisettes,* after the blue-grey stuffs seamstresses wore at the time. We were young and poor, but we knew how to work. We were the first true independents. With us poverty was charming.

"Saucy innocents we were. Poets praised us. Our feet were fine and elegant. You couldn't tell them from a line between our skirts and the carpet. Our gowns, madras cotton and flowered lawn, rustled like music. Our petticoats exploded like milkweed from a pod." The listeners inspected the old storyteller, straining to imagine charm in her gaunt frame.

"We wore caps of flowing ribbons. Admirers thought our coifs were done by masters in filigree." Her guests gaped at the disheveled head. "Our lives were romance. Not like today where *cocottes* trick gentlemen into paying their rent and clothing bills. For a few sous we sewed all day, making frocks look like the nightgown of the bride of Lamermoor. We delivered our creations along the boulevards, directing our profiles toward passersby. We had style and courage! Our patter was outrageous. It enchanted the artists of bohemia and dandies in their vests of iridescent brocade. They gathered on corners, peering through spy glasses to isolate our adorable silhouettes from the rest of the crowd." She sighed.

"Our loves were boys our own age, happy like we were to be free. The young jackals swore they'd give us anything. All we got was their arm as we strolled among the windmills of Montmartre," she cackled. "We lived like gods in attics above Paris. We didn't mind being temporary wives. Of course, the students soon abandoned us for more respectable brides chosen by their parents, which made us sad, but not for long.

"One of my gallants was a poet in love with the Middle Ages. He showed me daggers hanging in his room and read me lines he wrote in a dissecting theater, or after a night in the cemetery." She bent over the candle, calculating its bestial effect on her face:

By Hell! I feel an immense desire
To grind her flesh between my teeth, and seize
Her half-decayed heart from her gaping breast
With some or other shred of her blue-green skin.

"I couldn't but love him! My poet promised that after I died, he'd toast my memory by drinking punch from my beautiful little skull." She smiled into the darkness while the visitors, feigning fear, poked each other.

"My friends ended up worse than me. Consumption got some, like Mimi the water drinker or the lady of the camellias. Many went to Saint-Lazare for theft, vagrancy, or prostitution." She looked up for a reaction. "Some were experiments for Dr Charcot at the Salpêtrière asylum. Many made regular marriages and plenty are living off properties from gentlemen they bewildered when they were young. Back then, I was loved and respected. Some day I expect to receive a fabulous inheritance." When, and who from? Caroline's audience squirmed. They would wait and come back. They stared at the rags on the wall, hiding greedy faces with smiles.

Gnawing impatience made some of these guests fall on the old *grisette*. Pretending to be drunk they fondled her, hoping to find a purse. They thought of squashing her like a moth, slashing her mattress, drinking wine from her "little skull."

* * *

By 1900 Caroline-Céleste Fourmentin was receiving ten francs a month from public assistance. She supplemented this with prostitution and begged from various businesses. Depending on others for necessities offended her to the core. Madame Pinel, the grocer, meaning to be kind, treated the old lady like a cretin. "Come for your scraps today, Aunt Caroline?" she'd say, so the housewives in her shop could overhear. The Good Samaritan, Caroline thought, waiting for her handout. "Merci, Madame." Taking her package, she proceeded to the café of Monsieur Daligny. "Here's your jar of water and a packet of tea, Mère Fourmentin," he'd say. "Mère Fourmentin says thank you," she parroted.

Around noon on a sunny day in May, Madame Pinel and Monsieur Daligny wondered why the old lady hadn't come for her supplies. They met in the street and decided to walk to her field. No one answered their calls, so they pushed away the carpet in the doorway of the shed. Silence. They pulled down the rags in the windows. A nauseating smell. Aprons to their noses, they peered inside. It was too dark to see. They raised a lighted match. They'd read melodramas in the newspapers, but they weren't prepared for this.

On a straw mattress lay Caroline. A huge liver, glistening like anthracite, rested on her stomach. Hanging in pearly skeins on the wall above her cot were six meters of intestines. "Why this must be *tripe*!" cried Monsieur Daligny. "Surely, it's not … *hers*!" Falling on each other, the merchants raced to town.

They wailed the news to two policemen returning after an exciting day at the annual steeplechase. The officers stormed the shanty, slipping on Caroline's blood. Parisian sportsmen also returning from the track, chatting about Merry Boy who broke his leg and had to be shot, passed the Pont de la Puce and saw uniforms. At the shed they saw the real spectacle of the day.

* * *

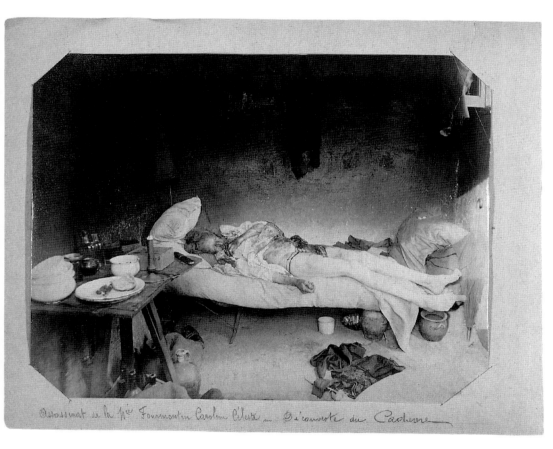

Assassinat de la f^{lle} Fourmentin Caroline Céleste — Découverte du Cadavre

MURDER OF FOURMENTIN, CAROLINE-CÉLESTE

Discovery of the body

"Rape! Murder! Evisceration! Jack the Ripper's back!" Reporters pummeled their readership. Dr Socquet, the medical examiner, described the crime like a connoisseur, attributing death to strangulation after finding marks on the old lady's neck. Then, he reasoned, fearing she hadn't died from rape and suffocation, the brute cut her open, plunged in his hand and pulled out her guts plus the liver. Motive? "It's a mistery," was all he could say.

Sadistic tramp mad on absinthe? Vampire? Chief detective Cochefert didn't know. Faced with reporters he stalled. "Revolting crime, twelve or thirteen years ago. I was chief of police in Saint-Ouen, and a maniac in the cemetery dug up the blackened body of a prostitute, opened her stomach and gave free rein to his unbalanced instincts." The press strung together other fables.

Le Petit Parisien: "Aunt Caroline hated tramps and vagrants. She chased them away with a stick. She hardly went out, except for provisions, and traded her services to the sick in the community for alms and vegetables." *Le Petit Journal:* "The victim had a bohemian sense of hospitality, often taking in odious vagrants and tramps who appealed to her sympathy." Such speculation entertained the public until the police found something, but they never did.

* * *

The photographs taken by Monsieur Dugast, Bertillon's delegate, show the walls of Caroline's shanty blackened from oil lamps and a bad stove. In death the old seamstress looks remarkably graceful. Her great height, now horizontal, out-scales the hut. A shift, pulled above her waist, exposes slender legs which extend beyond the cot. In the photographer's explosive flash the legs look cool and white as marble. An arm raised to her chest is the gesture of combat.

The things show poverty and distress, but also something else, the unmistakable style of the *grisette*. Plenty of popular illustrations portray the humble room of the working girl as positively alluring. The old lady's dwelling is a travesty. A foul pallet mocks the *grisette*'s idealized cot. Her garret would have been papered in pale pink stripes alternating with floral ribbons, not shreds of skirt, shift or apron. An enameled wash stand would have held a white ironstone bowl and pitcher, not stinking crockery. A single candle and pretty hat would have hung on the wall, not six meters of intestines. The *grisette* of legend would have put flowered cloth in her window for privacy, not rags against mean weather. She would have turned a pretty profile toward the handsome blond visitor in shirt sleeves, removing boots with a boot shoe, not fallen under the blade of a sadist.

Caroline's interior is an inventory of making ends meet. On the table scissors have been taken from their oval toilet case. There are chipped porcelain plates, a cup, breakfast bowls. Under the table — clay jugs, corked bottles. A pair of coarse shoes are the current equivalent of the *grisette*'s fabled feet. She found in the abandoned field, flowering with currant bushes, more than a final home; she recovered the memory of a former garret. Her only adornment, besides the copper ring, was a tortoise shell comb. Her shanty was not the protected attic above the city. It was the nest of a ground bird, open to jaws that tore her apart.

17 The Gift

4 December 1900, 205 Rue du Faubourg
Saint-Denis, X[th] Arrondissement, torso and
thighs of a 17- to 25-year-old man found
wrapped in red fabric, brown moleskin,
and grey wrapping paper. A head, two arms
and two legs wrapped in a horse blanket,
waxed cloth, and wrapping paper found on
the same day in the Rue des Platrières,
XIth Arrondissement. Suspects never charged.
Insufficient evidence.

The Universal Exhibition has just closed, and Paris is still reeling from
the fair to end all fairs. This had been a balance sheet of the past
century, extravagant proof that the assets of civilization far outweighed
the liabilities. A huge statue on the triumphal entrance had proclaimed
the world's enthusiasm. The figure did not personify Liberty, Abun-
dance, or even Technology. She was all too familiar, a pretty girl with
open arms. Smiling muse of the moment, *La Parisienne* welcomed fifty
million visitors to 80,000 exhibits glorifying modern paradise.

Electric sidewalks had propelled spectators through part of the
vast acreage and its stupefying detail. The most attended display was a
perfectly simulated Swiss village, with papier-maché mountains and a
hundred real peasants. Second in popularity were a pavilion of historic
costumes and a reconstruction of the streets of Old Paris. Yet the most

spectacular was the white stucco temple dedicated to the goddess of electricity. Covered with thousands of incandescent bulbs, it rivaled the heavens in a perpetual fireworks display over the Champ de Mars. The Palace of Electricity, supreme testament of power over darkness, was the exhibition's promise that in the magic of new times every corner of the globe, guided by scientific truth, would radiate with clarity.

France was proud to be in the vanguard of this dream. By the end of 1900, two million French homes burned electric lights. Thirty thousand telephones were in service. And in less than five months since its opening, the new Metropolitan subway line had carried fifteen million passengers between Vincennes and Neuilly. There were the inevitable mishaps, of course. The underground transit had already electrocuted several passengers, leading cynics to rename the Metropolitan the "*Nécro*politan" in a fit of black humor, while others asserted that the world was still a treacherous place, and despite the overwhelming optimism, civilized races constituted only a heroic minority against unknown forces.

* * *

It is the first week of Advent. Parisians are looking forward to Christmas candles and Yule logs. But the newspapers have begun to circulate dark news. On the morning of 5 December, two little boys, following the Rue Sorbier on their way to school, noticed on the Rue des Platrières a large package in a ditch filled with debris. The package seemed the size of a child. One boy, hoping to free the captive inside, asked a passerby to cut the string. The paper fell open. Out dropped a filthy hand. The gentleman ran for the police commissioner who carried the package to his office. He pulled back the rest of the wrappings: a severed head, two arms, and two legs cut off at the knees.

At the same moment, along the railroad yards of the Gare du Nord, at 205 Rue du Faubourg Saint-Denis, a maid came down to buy milk. She saw a large, carefully tied package behind the carriage entrance to the courtyard and alerted the concierge. The package was too heavy for the women to lift, so they asked a policeman to cut the string. A mutilated human torso was revealed. The policeman ran for Monsieur Maurice, police commissioner of this quarter, who arrived with his secretary.

To Maurice the torso looked like the work of Jack the Ripper. A terrible gash extended from chest to stomach. Blood still flowed from the neck and stumps of the arms and legs. The flesh was still soft and cool, as if the crime had occurred a few hours before. Maurice rewrapped the torso and placed it at the bottom of the stairs facing the concierge's station. He closed the door of the building and had a policeman stand guard while he telephoned Cochefert.

* * *

There were five or six of them. They staged the sacrifice on the day of St Barbara, patron of metal workers, miners, and armorers. The victim had to have no past, present, or future. They found a boy their own age, about seventeen, dirty and homeless. They didn't know his name. They'd seen him on the edge of the city, hanging around public gardens where he had sex in the toilets with whomever he could. Sometimes he asked for money. He was starving. His arms were thin. He had little hands, and his feet were distorted from wearing shoes that were too small. Aimless and abject, he was otherwise completely invisible.

The boy had a pliable feminine air which excited and repelled them. After dark they lured him to their shanty in Ménilmontant with promises of wine and sex. He followed where they led. St Barbara is supposed to protect the faithful from sudden death. The boy wasn't one of the faithful.

When they had him inside, they doused him with water to surprise him. As he shuddered, they stunned him with a blow on the head and cut his throat. No one was solely responsible for the violence. It was a collective act.

Everything important began after the boy's death. They dismembered him with sharp knives, quickly and artfully, like professional butchers under a spell. They paid special attention to the head. Cutting it from the torso, they transformed it by stripping off the scalp and removing the nose and upper lip. They left the ears, which floated on each side of his face like newly hatched butterflies. Gazing at the head they fell in love with the sweetness of the victim's expression which, in contrast to his wretched life, showed in death an almost divine calm. They hacked off his arms at the shoulders and cut off his legs at the knees.

Attacking the torso with a fierce stroke from sternum to abdomen, they cut off the genitals, pulled out the intestines and the large liver, which they put aside with the trophies of nose, lips, and scalp.

They collected all the pieces, not to bury or throw away. They had a plan more majestic than their tawdry lives would have deemed possible. They never talked about this but worked together in perfect harmony, as if they had. Putting aside the smaller trophies, they divided the larger body parts into two groups.

They wrapped the head, arms, and legs in a horse blanket with a red domino design. They covered this with an impermeable piece of waxed moleskin, to which they added a third layer of grey wrapping paper. They tied the package neatly with strong cord.

They prepared the torso as they had the other dismembered parts. They wrapped it in a red curtain, which still had the metal rings attached, and covered this with a waxed tarpaulin, black on one side and white on the other, like those used by delivery boys. For the final layer they used the same grey paper as the first package, and secured it with strong cord.

They drew lots to determine who would get the scalp, genitals, nose, intestines, and the glistening liver, which became organs of divination, precious talismans. Their deeds were vicious only in terms of the city's institutions and laws. They were appeasing sterner gods than the goddess of electricity, or the silly maiden on the triumphal

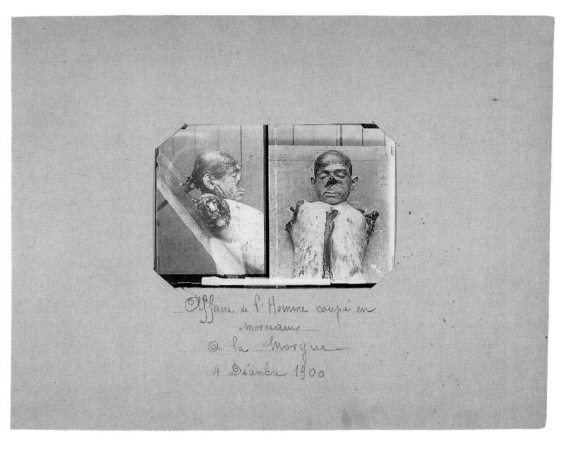

Affaire de l'Homme coupé en
morceaux
à la Morgue
4 Décembre 1900

AFFAIR OF THE MAN CUT IN PIECES

At the morgue
4 December 1900

arch of the exposition. They exposed this modern fakery by carving up a single victim and declaring darkness a permanent fact.

The young murderers, whose confidence lay in their solidarity, viewed the next phase of their ritual with the same care as they did the apportionment of the small souvenirs. They presented the packages to the city of Paris to mark the end of the first year of the new century. They saw their gesture as divinely beautiful because they took so much trouble to accomplish it.

They had long discussions about where to deposit the packages and were open about making their deliveries. Pretending to be laborers, they left the shack where they committed the crime wearing blue blouses and caps. One carried an umbrella. It was early morning. They walked with firm strides like athletes, bearing the packages on their shoulders. Stopping to talk under a street lamp, they noticed someone watching them from a window on the corner of the Rue des Panoyaux and the Rue des Platrières.

Scouting the site of their first deposit, they bumped into a man who thought they were laundry boys and casually asked why at this hour they hadn't finished their deliveries. One told the man to mind his own business, and when he tried to respond, another punched him to the ground, which had the desired effect because the man got up quickly and left. They returned to the others. After a short conference, one carried a package down the stairs from the Rue des Platrières and placed it in a ditch.

They walked westward to the Gare du Nord. A passerby on his way to work saw one of them leave the entrance to 205 Rue du Faubourg Saint-Denis, along the railway yards, and join two or three others. This was all he saw. Having delivered both packages, the conspirators went to a cabaret on the Rue de Dunkerque and waited.

* * *

Cochefert, always practicing his hobby of sleight-of-hand magic, is familiar with illusion, talking heads, women sawed in half, and other feats which conclude with the victim miraculously restored to the sound of thundering applause. A real cut up body, too ghastly to contemplate, was another story, but Cochefert had a special feeling about the man cut in pieces. The packages suggested to his colleagues two separate crimes. He insisted the remains belonged to one person. Even without mustache or genitalia the victim wasn't female: it had a strong lower lip.

The body parts were taken to the morgue and preserved in re-frigerators. The police want a name for this human debris, a person with origins and a history. The cool execution of the atrocity has them confused. It threatens to spread a contagion of violence they fear could erupt anywhere, any time. They want reasons. They believe in scien-tific criminal investigation with correct procedures, observation, and measurements. They want facts that get revenge.

Monsieur Dugast of the photographic service makes pictures. Dr Socquet, the medical examiner, establishes an approximate body weight of only forty-five kilograms and a height of between one meter fifty-eight to sixty. From the eyebrows and lashes he identifies the hair color as light chestnut. He analyzes the contents of the stomach: "A professional butcher did this. He knew enough to remove the intestines which would keep the body fresh for forty-eight hours." Socquet doesn't wonder why anyone would try to ensure this freshness.

Bertillon tries to put the boy's pieces together to get a precise measurement that will correspond to pre-recorded numbers on a recidivist's card. Anyone who ends up like this is surely on file. Bertillon hates this kind of body. Too many bits are missing for him to act with his usual brilliance.

He measures the ears, toes, and hands in order to apply his statistics. He's bothered by the loss of the scalp and strange blotches on the head, which don't allow him to compare it to the spectrum of skin colors on his charts. He's frustrated because the lost nose and upper lip ruin the profile, making proportional calculations impossible. Robbed of details that ignite his intelligence, Bertillon feels a pall around the human pile that nothing can penetrate. He's forced to tell the press that regarding identity, he has nothing definite.

To comfort the master of measurement, Monsieur Gaud, the morgue registrar, suggests that a wax sculptor in the anatomy department of the medical school might restore the head by adding a wax nose, lips, and hair so it will look like something Bertillon can evaluate, someone who'd lived and breathed.

Cochefert pieces together a disgusting vagrant of no more than seventeen. The teeth are white, well-planted. The face is beardless, the brows fair and thin. The boy has never worked. The hands are filthy but have no callouses. The fingernails are long and broken, the arms and legs stunted. The feet are small.

In a fine December rain, Monsieur André, examining magistrate for the case, visits the place where the children found the first package. Dugast stands on the footbridge overlooking the street, pointing his camera toward this site, a littered, wedge-shaped pit. His picture includes a sparse crowd and some gendarmes with pill-box hats and capes, one of whom guards the stairs to the bridge. The photographer also includes people gathered on balconies and others below them peering over walls. Having read about the sensational crime in the newspapers they've come to stare at the machine of justice.

Under an umbrella, André follows the Rue Sorbier, writing his impressions in a notebook. He copies down inscriptions on the walls. They suggest a meeting place for vagrants who identify themselves in bizarre script: "Henri Charles," called "Recdegas," appears below a drawing of a large bleeding heart pierced with a knife. "Emile," called "Petit Nain," little dwarf, appears next to "Joseph Henri," called "La Loi," the law, "March 1900." The magistrate gives these to the newspapers so they can give the crime a flavor that excites readers. André and the photographer go to the Rue du Faubourg Saint-Denis where the torso was found. Positioning his tripod opposite number 205, Dugast under his dark cloth attracts a group of tea and coffee merchants whom he includes in his photograph.

Affaire de l'homme coupé en morceaux – 205 f⁹ S! Denis – Endroit où il a été trouvé une partie des Débris

AFFAIR OF THE MAN CUT IN PIECES

205 Faubourg Saint-Denis, place where some of the remains were found

No one has sent the usual letter declaring responsibility. The police are overwhelmed by doubt. They have no idea who the victim is, why he was killed, or who is to blame. The discovery of a man cut in pieces, in the wake of the largest of all world exhibitions proclaiming Paris the source of light and progress, is a sinister joke.

In desperation the police call on a source of intelligence for which they harbor a certain contempt. They invite the public to see the remains of the young man cut in pieces. They don't display actual body parts. They're afraid the smell of decomposing flesh will be too frightening. No one has done the wax restorations. Bertillon has all but given up calculating, and besides, a completed head might look too much like a waxworks celebrity. Instead they give the public a salon experience, instructing them to shuffle past easels mounted with Dugast's large photographs. All show the man cut in pieces, natural size: head alone; arms and legs; and the third picture shows the head jammed on the torso in an attempt to suggest its living appearance.

Someone will spot him. A mother, father, co-worker will stop before the mutilated face and call out its name. Ten thousand people push through the doors the first day. The police have trouble controlling the crowd who come half-hoping for *le grand guignol,* a ghoulish amusement of morbid marionettes. As they fix on the boy's coagulated blood, rendered black in the pictures, and study his serene expression, which seems entirely out of keeping with the punishments he's suffered, they feel trapped in a conspiracy. Nothing restores him as a person or suggests reasons for the crime. What they confront is a grim approximation. A nonentity carved into human meat. The crowd becomes a howling mob. Some faint and have to be removed to the street. Children, shielded from the pictures but infected by the hysteria, urinate in the hall.

Every day, throughout Paris, human detritus is discovered which never goes on public display or receives benediction. Legs, feet, hands, and arms are collected behind restaurants by garbage men, by

Affaire de l'homme coupé en morceaux. Rue des Platrières. Endroit où a été trouvée une autre partie des débris

AFFAIR OF THE MAN CUT IN PIECES

Rue des Platrières, place where more remains were found

conductors on the Metropolitan subway and on trams. Gardeners find them in public parks. Children kick them like toys in empty lots. They're the catch of fishermen on the Seine. Unsuspecting citizens report receiving human skulls in the mail. The quarry is taken to the morgue and quietly disposed of. There are exceptions: a "virile member," found in a first-class railway carriage, belonging to "Monsieur Ducrocq," was recorded and returned to him. The noblest thing that happens to the rest is that it is recorded, year by year, month by month, day by day, in the extravagant script of a morgue clerk.

After the display of the man cut in pieces, scores of people, claiming to have lost relatives, applied to the morgue. The brother of George Goué, a seventeen-year old butcher missing since 1 December, arrived from Vincennes hoping to recognize his sibling. But he was too frightened to enter the room with the remains. An Englishman seeking his twenty-seven-year old son, came before the corpse-puzzle but did not recognize it as his child. Nor did the family of Octave Fournier, or fifteen others with missing children.

The crowd, although disgusted by the photographs, continued to be fascinated by the man cut in pieces, whose flesh began to assume a magical status. When the body parts were finally washed, and Dr Socquet published a statement listing the victim's marks and scars, 600 more people left elaborate descriptions for the morgue registrar to compare with the list. Needless to say, all this provided the applicants with nothing more than the little thrill they were really looking for.

* * *

Cochefert is peeling a hard-boiled egg and worrying about his foundering reputation as a representative of justice. His younger associate, Sub-Chief Hamard, is the kind of detective everyone loves. Hamard "devours" crime. He leaps from windows onto rooftops, seizing suspects cowering behind chimneys. By comparison, Cochefert is an ox.

He pays informers to finger three vagrants whom he arrests for theft, blustering to reporters that he won't release their names. "We can't alert their accomplices." The vagrants emphatically deny any role in the crime. He lets them go. The whole thing is bogus, but it gives Cochefert time to reflect.

Huge in his overcoat, he visits the Rue des Platrières. Long ago it cut through gypsum quarries where the fires of plaster kilns were an incense of suffocating fumes. Now the street is a bleak funnel, populated by outcasts. Cochefert circles the pit where the children found the first package.

He inspects the writing on the walls. "The Law," "Little Dwarf," and other names lead him toward Notre-Dame-de-la-Croix. From the top of the stairs joining the church to the hamlet of Ménilmontant below, he surveys the sordid hovels where he knows the crime must have taken place. The clock tower chimes the hour. He pokes his walking stick through the muddy pathways, turning over pieces of paper, abandoned tools, bits of crockery, straining to see faces in the lamplight of the shanties.

One night, with Notre-Dame-de-la-Croix back-lighted by the moon, Cochefert raids a shanty. He and ten agents find some young people sleeping among piles of stolen bicycles. The detective and his men tear up mattresses, throw pots and pans against the walls. He wants to frighten these children. Roused from sleep, they have the expressions of angels. He arrests them for theft. One carries a sharpened dagger protected by a piece of linen.

He should take them to the prefecture. He decides to question them in their hole. He's looking at the killers. Every inch of him feels it. He watches them get comfortable in their chairs, blow cigarette smoke into the lamp, stare at the floor. Studying the hands which stunned the victim and cut him up, he looks for marks from the hallowed weapons. He smells murder in their dirty clothes. He can practically hear the whispers of these goaders playing with their twitching toy. If the walls could speak, he'd have a confession.

Léon Cholley, the leader, gives his address as 8 Rue des Platrières. The street of the first package. Cochefert decides that Cholley and his companion, Lucie Navarre, both twenty-three, are the authors of the crime. Their associates are Louis Mille, called "Coco," eighteen; Pierre Millot, called "La Chatte," sixteen; and Alfred Tissu, twenty-three. Tissu, or "Morand," is wanted for robbery in Lyons.

Cochefert surveys the soot-covered ceiling. A hole but no slaughterhouse. How did they make the evidence disappear? He remembers "The Mystery of Dr Lynn," an illusion he loves at the Folies-Bergère. A pretty woman, cut off from view at the thighs, rests on a small swinging shelf. The shelf disappears, and the woman, half-length, is suspended in mid-air. The crowd looks in vain for the rest of the body. Intense electric light against black velvet is the secret. Cochefert is always dazzled. The body of the woman is actually stretched out behind her. No one sees it because the light on her torso is so bright.

He must not let the light of these sneering faces blind him. Darkness will reveal the signs. He chews an egg and studies his opponents. They're strong and agile. La Chatte gives obscene answers to his questions. "I've been waiting to be arrested!" Coco bellows. Cochefert's agents punch them into their chairs, but the killers are laughing at them. He finds clean blue workers' smocks and an umbrella under the beds, which tells him everything but nothing about murder.

Lucie Navarre is an appealing little tart. In the middle of Cochefert's questions she jumps on a table and flings her legs into a *cancan*, singing, wiggling her backside, like a wild animal protecting her young.

Cholley calls himself "The Angelus." *Angelus domini nuntiavit Mariae.* He wants to see if the fat man recognizes the prayer in his name. Flamboyant epithets are underworld chic, another language to decipher. Cochefert doesn't bother. He knows every brutality required to extract confessions. He doesn't want to crack their illusion. Moonlight glances off the walls of the shanty. He sees only the electric light and black velvet of insolent children.

The public wants results. Cochefert finds not a drop of blood, nothing linking this company to the butchery of the squalid boy. They're better magicians than he is. He releases Coco and La Chatte. He sends Morand to the judge in Lyons and Lucie back to Ménilmontant. He holds Cholley and visits him in his cell. They make small talk while Cochefert's agents, worried about the irregularities of his investigations, press their ears to the wall. "Are you satisfied?" asks the Angelus.

"Are you?"

"I feel we succeeded."

Cochefert fears asking what this means. Cholley has him. He doesn't know how or why. "Release him." No fanfare. No applause.

* * *

Late in March 1902 André turned his file over to the court clerk, officially shelving the case. Hoaxers continued to sprout. *Le Figaro* reported the arrest in Tours of someone "strongly suspected ... the three-hundred-and-fifty-second new lead in the case in sixteen months." To Cochefert, the confessing maniacs were aftershock, spasms from incomprehensible forces. He was embarrassed, but only when he thought of how he looked to his superiors. Otherwise, he had to laugh. He can make giraffes talk.

Well after the Great War, the man cut in pieces lingered in the minds of the police. Perhaps they felt they owed him something, because an enlargement of his noseless head came to be hung with assorted photographs of weapons, murderers, and crime scenes in many "criminal museums" of the prefectures. In such exhibitions, the boy, terrifying in his serene sleep, reminded experts of the human heart that some crimes, though cruel, have nothing to do with solutions.

18 An Englishman Comes to Town

12–13 April 1901, 29 Avenue Henri-Martin,
XVIth Arrondissement, aborted robbery
and attempted murder by blows and stabbing
of Madame Louise Kolb, 39, former actress
and courtesan, by Henry Gilmour, alias
Edward Smith, 49, plumber's assistant,
pickpocket, professional burglar. Sentenced
to forced labor for life.

Every day at three, Louise Kolb telephones Albert, her chauffeur-mechanic in the apartment opposite, and orders him to get out his polishing cloth. She descends to the courtyard, and he helps her into her new automobile. Then they drive, at the legal limit of ten kilometers an hour, through the Bois-de-Boulogne.

Madame Kolb is an avid sportswoman. She takes this motor ride for the benefits of fresh air. She also uses it to maintain her position as an arbiter of chic among a wide circle of friends and acquaintances.

She spends several hours constructing a fabulous toilette, carefully choosing jewels that will enhance her *décolletage* while seated in the modern vehicle. Albert, rudely handsome, is essential to the effect. She's pleased by his devotion. When bothering to consider it, she thinks he may be in love with her.

Madame Kolb is a former actress with a comfortable expense account. She looks twenty-eight. At thirty-nine she has a daughter, Madame Fynch, married to an English insurance broker and living in London. She is also about to become a grandmother for the second time. In diaphanous *déshabillé* Madame Kolb receives at least ten people a day in her beautiful Passy apartment. Many come from the cream of French society. She affects snobbism with this élite, flattering its vanity by conversing in flawless English.

She also affects honorability. At present she favors the very respectable Dr Schultzberger, who enters her flat with his own key, sometimes staying the night. A string of such gentlemen over the years have provided her with an apartment, a smart but discreet villa in Maisons-Lafitte, an allowance, jewels, and of course, her automobile.

Other men with vaguer capabilities also figure in her entourage. She doesn't bother to find out if they're pimps or petty thieves. She chats them up in the patois, thrilling to their coarse profiles. Brown-haired Georges is a very nice boy with dazzling white teeth. And there is Georges K. who comes often to dine and, like the doctor, may stay till morning. If anyone were to ask her maid, Madeleine Fourcade, how many suspicious visitors crossed Madame Kolb's threshold, the girl would have to say that the list was too long to name them all.

With Schultzberger currently paying the bills, Madeleine arranges the others' comings and goings with precise timing. Besides, her mistress hired her on the sole condition of her absolute silence regarding what went on in the house.

Madame Kolb brings her diamonds to all the international pleasure spots, never hesitating to mention the marvelous adornments she was forced, by discretion, to leave in her safe. Before her trip to Monte-Carlo last winter she met a man whom she described excitedly to her friend Madame d'España.

"Another one? You attach yourself too easily," scolded the confidante.

"Bah! So what?" scoffed the former actress. "He's pretty, and I think he has money." But soon she declared the new plaything was a bore.

"What's wrong? I thought he had millions."

"He's a *panderer*," said Madame Kolb, making her point in English, drawing on her cigarette and pretending he never existed.

* * *

Edward Smith has no home. He's not sure where he was born. He thinks it was Fulham in London. His parents, whoever they were, abandoned him to the streets. He survived by stealing which led to other little jobs. At forty-nine he's a professional.

Smith has a light step. He speaks softly through his teeth in clipped phrases. He looks like a sportsman, medium build, brown hair, divided by a side part, prominent apple-red cheeks, pointed nose, small chin. On his upper lip is the thick brush of a mustache. He could be taken for the coach of a champion cyclist, except for his eyes. Small and piercing, they seem buried under his brows, as if waiting in ambush.

His hands reveal more of his history than his face. They're misshapen from hard labor in a string of prison terms, which total nearly half his life. In Adelaide, Melbourne, Sydney, and Bendigo, Australia: "I found myself with bank notes I couldn't account for," he'd tell the judge. By 1894 he was in London, breaking and entering. The court, ignorant of his previous offenses, gave him only three months. Robbing again got him seven more years. He passed the time reading Dickens and Walter Scott. His vocabulary shows a literary flair. He prefers the word "engage" to "hire."

He told French police his name was Edward Smith. Under duress he says his original surname might have been Robinson. He's on record in Australia as "Henry Smith" and "Henry Gilmour." He's also known as "George Sweeny" and "James Wilson."

Burglary is Smith's specialty. He loathes the thought of killing anyone. After breaking and entering on two continents, his gear has a certain perfection he calls "humanitarian." He's assembled ingenious devices, unknown in Europe, he's proud to say, like the copper ball covered with orange rind and attached to a length of elastic, which he uses as a kind of sling shot. The orange rind softens the metal so its impact won't break the skull. If he has to strike he only wants to daze whoever gets in the way. He likes the small bag of sand he carries in his pocket. It's solid enough to throw someone off balance so he can grab what he wants, but soft enough not to cause permanent damage. Afterward, he cuts open the bag and lets out the sand. If he's searched there's no weapon, just a piece of cloth.

In late March 1901 Smith was walking the streets of London after his last sentence. He was thinking he might stay a while when he met a friend from the Sydney days who said he knew a woman looking for someone to pull an important job in Paris. This woman turned out to be a brown-haired gentleman called Wilson, who wore a top hat and was impeccably attired. Wilson thought Smith comported himself in the most correct manner imaginable. He engaged him on the spot.

Smith's clothes were lamentable after years behind bars. Wilson bought him a new suit, an overcoat of black wool twill, two celluloid collars, two shirts, and a soft black felt hat, which made Smith feel as he liked to feel, invisible. They took the ferry to Paris. Wilson, who was paying, insisted on changing hotels each day. Smith noticed he always registered them under the name of Chanticleer.

Smith liked Paris. Lots of pretty houses to rob, and plenty of crowds for disappearing in. With his record, France was the place if he got unlucky. The guillotine seemed a nobler way to end up than the misery of London prisons or the Newgate gallows. Wilson said they'd have to wait a couple of weeks while he staked the coup. To feel at home Smith went to the races.

Soon Wilson showed Smith a map of the apartment he was engaged to rob. It belonged to Madame Louise Kolb, a former actress

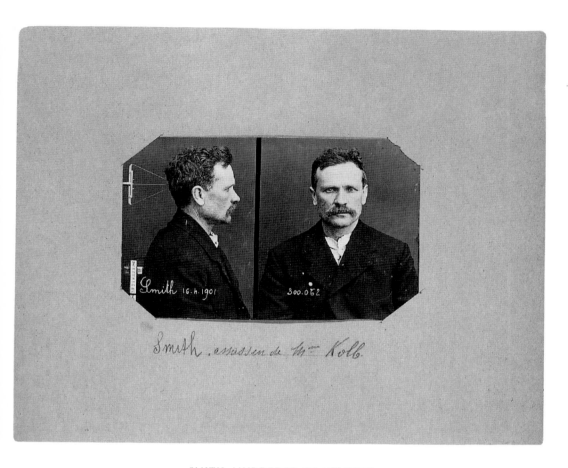

SMITH, MURDERER OF MME KOLB

who lived on 35,000 francs a year from her investments and additional gifts from a string of admirers. She had more money than that, and beautiful jewels were locked in her salon safe. The keys to this safe were in an Empire secretary in her bedroom. Smith didn't ask Wilson how he knew this, if he was a friend, or someone she'd met by chance. He didn't ask why a friend would rob a friend. He didn't care.

Wilson knew the lady's habits perfectly. Every day at three she motored in the Bois-de-Boulogne. Wilson and Smith went to her address at 29 Avenue Henri-Martin and stood outside. She kept them waiting until five. Smith saw a veiled woman, lavishly dressed for an outing, covered in gold and jewels, helped into her car by a lackey.

When she safely turned the corner, they took the stairs to the second floor. Wilson said the maid would be in her room on the sixth. He took a key from his pocket and opened the door. Smith noted it wasn't a burglar's key but a real one.

The apartment was huge, full of fancy furnishings. Smith was amazed. Wilson said this was nothing. She also had a stylish house where she spent the summer. Wilson pushed Smith inside. "She's got the keys. Get them when she's asleep. We'll meet later." And he disappeared.

Smith checked his tools wrapped in newspaper: a brace and bit, a crowbar, scissors, steel wire cutters to cut the electric lines and door bells, a cord tied in a running knot attached to a gold ring on his left hand, the bag of sand, the copper ball.

He prospected the apartment, looking for places to hide. There were plenty of couches and settees. He lay under them all, testing the view. The bathroom also looked good. There was a clothes rack piled with dressing gowns he could get behind. He could sleep in this room if he had to.

At seven Smith heard women's laughter. He was in the salon, checking the lock on the secretary. He scooted under a settee and sniffed their rustling skirts, wondering which he'd come to rob. Peering through a silk fringe he saw a woman lock a set of keys in the

Empire secretary. That must be the actress, he thought, and while her back was turned slipped into the bathroom.

Smith had a fierce hunger. It got worse when Madame Kolb dined on champagne, tripe, and chicken Marengo, served by the maid. From the vestibule he watched how she licked a pretty mouth while eating a plum. He noted the undulation of her swan's neck as she giggled at a naughty story told by her guest, Madame d'España. After this lady left, someone let himself into the apartment. Smith listened as Madame Kolb dallied for a few hours with a man she called, "dear doctor!"

The doctor departed. Madame Kolb gave her maid instructions for the next day's dinner party. Smith watched as the lady undressed for bed. He trembled at the scents in her clothes. Sweet wood violets came to mind as she loosened long brown hair. Liberated from her corset, her body dissolved in the light of her table lamp. He hadn't known many women. He was amazed at the pride of this French one, at the fearless way she appraised herself before the cheval glass which seemed to assure her that she was still beautiful and very desirable.

After she got in bed, Smith listened for the steady breathing of deep sleep. He was supposed to wait until five. Wilson said that was when the front door of the building would open for the delivery men, and he could escape as one of them. He was impatient. He'd been in this place too long, and he was ravenous.

In shirtsleeves and stocking feet he tiptoed into the bedroom. Wilson said the door would open without a sound. It made a terrible noise. Smith winced. It didn't wake her. Wilson said the floor boards were tight, but they groaned as Smith went to her secretary. His fingers were quick. He broke the lock in a flash and slipped the jewel safe keys into his pocket.

He was about to enter the salon for the stash when the sleeper sat up. "Who's there?" He pulled out the sandbag. In the dark he couldn't see what she was grabbing, but suddenly the room exploded with electric light. She screamed at the black demon standing in front of her. Smith's head was wrapped in black crepe to hide his features, another of his techniques. Seeing the secretary wide open, Madame Kolb screamed even louder and threw a knife she kept under her pillow. It missed.

Smith grabbed her by the throat to shut her up. But she had the lungs of a deep-sea diver. He hit her in the face with the sandbag. She found the weapon strange. Shaped like a sausage, it was hard and soft at the same time. It broke after smashing her face, spilling on the carpet.

Madame Kolb was dazed, badly bruised, and crying for help. Smith yanked out the copper ball covered with orange rind, attached to the elastic. He swung the contraption, but he was too energetic. The elastic broke, and the ball smacked her good and hard. Smith was confused, the sandbag broken, the ball on the other side of the room, her crying, and no booty. He didn't want to kill. He couldn't make her quiet. She flung herself over him like a bareback rider on a mount. He was amazed at her strength.

Wilson didn't tell him she was in superb physical shape. Madame Kolb rode horses in the Bois when she didn't drive in her automobile. She was renowned for gliding her animal over the most difficult obstacles. Frantic, Smith opened a vial of ether and flung it at her.

She grabbed at the bell pull to signal her maid. Smith punched her in the chest, which sent her flying. He was exhausted. So far, this contest's a draw, he thought. She lay panting. He collapsed on a chair, wondering what to do next.

The battle recommenced. Smith forgot about the gold ring on his finger attached to the cord with the running knot. It was too complicated to get around her neck. He took a chair and broke it over her head.

"What a skull!"

"You speak English!"

Horrified at the intimacy of the retort, at the possibility of ac-tually conversing with this amazon, he grabbed a stemmed glass from the night table and hit her again. It also reached its mark with too much force. Raining down, fine fragments lodged in her face, hands, and legs. One tore a tendon of Smith's right index finger. Appalled at the sight of his own blood, he stopped, realizing he was her prisoner.

The telephone began to ring, then the doorbell. Her cries had alerted the other apartments. Someone had phoned the police. The foyer was crowded with rescuers. He flew to his hiding place in the bathroom.

The servants of Madame Kolb's neighbors stormed the bedroom. They found her in a nightdress soaked with blood. Her hair covered deep cuts on her face. She was weak but clearly alive. "Where is the murderer? Where did he go?" Unable to speak, she lifted her hand and pointed shakily to the door of the *cabinet de toilette.*

Smith was writhing in pain and fury. Expecting the police he put on his frock coat and shoes. When the police commissioner opened the door he found Smith seated on a chair, using his handkerchief as a tourniquet to check the flow of blood from his finger. The authorities didn't trouble him in the least. "I came to rob not kill. If she hadn't awakened while I worked the secretary I wouldn't have tried to *brain her.*" He added that he didn't understand French.

* * *

Smith endures days of questioning with an interpreter and a lawyer from the British embassy neither of whom he trusts. He intimidates the magistrates with his distance and reluctance to elaborate, which seems to them like superior intelligence. He won't say how or where he spent his time before the robbery. He wants to be called Gilmour but won't say if Henry Gilmour is his real name. Smith insists he had an accomplice, repeating the story about Wilson. "He was one of her lovers who let me in with a key." But no one believes Wilson exists.

Madame Kolb is shown Bertillon's photograph of Smith. "Never have I encountered any man resembling this one. I can only wonder how he entered my home."

For weeks the newspapers give daily reports of Madame Kolb's condition. It is grave. She's sustained more than forty wounds, has a high fever, and alternates between prostration and delirium. Deep in bandages, her head and cheeks are badly gashed. Certain wounds reached the bone. Cut tendons have ruined her hands. She is being cared for by two nurses, her maid, and a team of doctors. They are injecting her with morphine to ease the pain. All visitors are barred. The police commissioner is told she's too fragile to answer his questions.

Madame Kolb is not only in pain, she's deeply apprehensive. Everyone is sympathetic, but they're wondering how this brutal burglar entered her apartment. Could she have let him in? She can't remember anybody named Wilson. She can't remember whom she's given keys to over the years.

After a couple of months she indicates she's ready to answer questions, but when the police arrive she finds she can't. Like Smith she becomes mute and obscure. If she names all those who visit her, she'll expose her habits, those of *tout Paris* and their friends in the underworld. She decides to remain silent and protect everyone from scandal. The papers are defaming her, suggesting she's not the actress she claims but something like a common whore. True enough, she only played a few minor roles.

Madame Kolb lives in dread. Everyone thinks she knew this brute who inflicted her terrible injuries, that their relations were more than superficial. He entered the apartment so easily. No one's saying so, but the obscure accomplice in a crime that nearly killed her seems to be none other than herself.

If Madame Kolb's silence cast doubt on her reputation, and the crime seemed a just reward for a woman of easy virtue, Smith-Gilmour's self-possession turned him into an exotic specimen. The newspapers speculated that if he'd been in Paris for the Universal Exhibition he would have had a *succès fou* as a British Hercules who assaults sleeping women with "humanitarian" devices.

At his trial Smith played the insulted guest, which had the lawyers for both sides turning cartwheels to show him hospitality, to impress him with the civility of French justice. There was no chance of him losing his head on the scaffold since his victim had survived, but they argued over it anyway. It seemed a shame that the Englishman couldn't understand the efforts being made on his behalf. Wouldn't he have been touched by their concern?

Madame Kolb's defender, Henri Robert, renowned for brilliantly defending some of the most dangerous criminals in the history of the Assizes, portrayed his client as the epitome of mercy. "It's the fervent wish of this generous victim that her attacker not be put to death."

Smith-Gilmour, coldest and most indifferent of spectators, understood nothing being said, but shouldn't he be glad to be so well-defended at the expense of this infamous creature? No one learned what he thought.

Madame Kolb was considered too fragile to appear as a witness, for which she was deeply grateful. But she heard reports of the smears against her used to curry favor with the Englishman.

The former actress slowly recovered in Maisons-Lafitte. On a chaise longue, wrapped in tartans, she watched the leaves from her horse chestnut trees blanket the lawns. In the fresh air she strolled a little and took brief drives in her car. Her forehead and both cheeks were permanently scarred. The wound on top of her head throbbed and refused to heal. She tried to read the current rage, Anna de Noailles' poems in *Le Cœur innombrable,* but the sentiments gave her a headache.

19 Too Many

21–22 April 1901, village of Corancez, ten
kilometers southeast of Chartres, five children
of Louis-Edouard Brière — Flora, 12, Béatrice,
11, Laurent, 7, Laure, 5, Célina, 4 — found
murdered in their beds. Brière, 42, a widower
with a failing threshing business, was tried
and sentenced to death. Sentence commuted
to forced labor for life.

First he cut the throat of his dog. Then he walked to Sauger's café
in the village and played cards. That April evening five customers
consumed four liters of wine. Brière wasn't drunk. Not even after
Heurtault invited him and his neighbor Lubin to taste the new wine
in his cellar. Afterward, Brière and Lubin strolled along the main road
to their farms on the outskirts of Corancez, splashing through puddles
from a recent downpour and gazing at the moon in silence while
everyone slept.

Lubin left around twelve-thirty to tend a sick cow. Brière crossed
the road, entered his courtyard, and put up the shutters on all the
windows of the house. He stepped over the corpse of Ravachol, a
black mutt with an ugly bark, named after the anarchist. Then he
went inside where five of his children were sleeping and smashed their
heads with an iron bar. Flora cried out. He took a knife, stabbed her,

and threw the body to the floor. Pulling linen from the cupboards, he spilled a bottle of ink.

He returned to the yard. With the knife used on Flora he cut his left hand and sliced the right side of his face. He flung his galoshes, scarf, and cap onto the manure with the knife and fell. "The pigs. They tried to kill me. They took my wallet. Robbed me of 1,500 francs! I'm dying!"

Lubin, in and out of bed because of his cow, heard no noise. But his dog woke him around three. Trying to calm the animal, frantically pacing at the gate, Lubin noticed Brière. "Is that you?" The shadow, who'd crawled to the road, was on its back.

Lubin ran for the Barons, nearby. As these neighbors tried to lead him to his bed, Brière protested. "Put me in the stable. I don't want my kids seeing me cut up like this. Ah, those wretches! They've killed me! I'll get in bed after my kids wake up." So they bandaged his head, gave him some brandy, and left.

In the stable Brière slept late. He awoke to find that his neighbors had entered the house and discovered massacred children and walls covered with brain. Some fled, horrified. Others called for the police in Chartres, ten kilometers away. Brière seemed surprised not to see his children. Noticing strangers — magistrates and policemen milling about — he collapsed and was taken to the hospital.

* * *

Investigators find a bucket by the pump full of red water and human tissue where the killer presumably washed his hands. The five victims, placed in the barn on a trestle table covered with straw, are a bloody soup, their arms still raised in gestures of defense. Béatrice turns toward her brother Laurent, lips pursed, as if to give him a final kiss. Laure and Célina's eyes are open, their mouths twisted into ghastly grins. The bodies have vertical gashes along the breasts, evidence of the coroner's prompt autopsies, which someone has tried to conceal with pansies and field flowers.

They find an ink bottle near the dead children. When arrested Brière had fresh ink on his hands. "It spilled while I was writing." They find an empty grain sack, covered with blood, under a pile of papers, and a small bloodied iron bar. In his yard is a jacket, the type that peasants wear on Sundays, its right sleeve covered with coagulated blood. "It's mine. I can't tell you why it's bloody." They show Brière a knife with a long blade, finely sharpened. His teeth are chattering. "It looks like one I had once. I killed a rabbit with it." An old plow blade with blood on it is also found in his yard. "Everyone has them. Perhaps it's mine, but I didn't bury it. What do you want me to tell you? I'm a stranger to all of this! I don't know what happened. I fainted."

In the house where the children's clothes are still folded on chairs from the night before, police scrape bloody remains from the walls and put them with the bodies into five oak caskets. They are interested in a letter they find from Germaine, 14, Brière's eldest child in Paris.

Everyone in Corancez knows Germaine Brière is her father's pet. He let her keep chickens and rabbits so she could use the profit to buy fashionable dresses; he gave her two new chicks to raise and trade for a new hat. She lives in Paris because Brière sent her to work in his sister Célina Destas's candy store-grocery on the Rue de Ménilmontant. Her letter is a response to her father's invitation to return home and visit: "I can't come now, Papa. Aunt has too much work for me to do." If the aunt had not saved her, there would have been six caskets.

* * *

Brière's bloody clothes have been seized as evidence. He won't wear those issued by the prison in Chartres, nor will he eat the food. "I can't survive on their potatoes and rice! I'm starving on their miserable soup!" He writes Lubin: "Send me fifty francs so I can get some meat from the canteen." He keeps his head in a cloth bandage and his arm in a sling, though the wounds are nearly healed.

241

Brière has admitted nothing. He insists he was assaulted by "two vagrants" of the kind who roam the plain of La Beauce, robbing the towns. Forty of these indigents have been questioned and released. Not the slightest suspicion links any of them to the murders.

Brière is receiving anonymous threatening letters. He paces his cell with a soldier's resolute step, refusing to speak to his cell mate. His guards are offended; he hasn't said ten words to them. He confides only in his lawyer, Monsieur Duparc, a young and inexperienced Chartres provincial.

Brière asks for picture books and is given a volume of *Le Magasin pittoresque*. He spends most of his time writing letters to friends and relatives. Such dispatches will arouse public sympathy, think his family. Brière seems to agree, for the correspondence is soon in the hands of the press. Challenged to interest city dwellers in this mysterious peasant during the months before the trial, reporters use one of these letters to conjure the tale of a country mouse.

5 May 1901

Dear brother and dear sister

I've seen Master Duparc; he told me you've taken the cows and the calf, as well as the pig and the rest of the beets. Give the animals the beets so they won't starve. The season's advancing. There's a bit of rye growing at the corner of the road. You can cut it and give it to them to eat. If you find that this inconveniences you too much you've only to tell Sauger to leave it and work the field.

As for things to wear, I don't have enough. I need my summer trousers, which should be in the bedroom armoire, my cap, which should be in the kitchen wall cupboard, a pair of socks, my braided wool slippers on the plank over the door of the house, and a tie or scarf in the bedroom armoire. I forgot to tell you that you can sell the pig, or if you need meat you can kill it if you want to. I end in wishing you all happiness,

Your brother, Brière Edouard

Brière's brother brings him a new blouse, dark grey pants, a rough wool cap, and eighty francs. "They took everything. You'll see." But the 600 francs pinned to his marriage contract are still there. And when agents search the walls of his house they find sheets of white metal forming an envelope, inside of which is a fifty-franc note, twenty-franc pieces, and other small change.

Those who had maintained his innocence are being swayed by the mounting evidence against him. Monsieur Martin, mayor of Corancez, announces, "If Brière committed this crime, he'll never admit it. I know him! I thought he was impeccable. I've since changed my mind!" The town tobacconist now thinks Brière is "capable of anything."

The village begins divulging old memories of a neighbor needing money. Thibaut, the local fireman, recalls coming to extinguish a fire in Brière's stable. He soon returned home, deciding he wasn't going to bother: when he arrived at the burning building, he'd seen Brière adding straw to the flames.

Others are revealing things more sinister. They suspect that for years he slowly poisoned his wife "with herbs." Brière had mistresses throughout La Beauce, not only in Corancez, but in villages around Morancez, Villemain, and Berchères-les-Pierres: "The young women of this village are hearty, ribald, and free. He met them at night."

From this harem Brière fell madly in love with "a scarecrow," Véronique Lubin, twenty-two, pale, sickly daughter of his neighbor. At dusk Brière joined her behind the barn. Véronique gave birth to a child, called Henri-Edouard. It lived but a few days. All assumed the father was Brière.

What his herbs partly achieved was completed by his wife's discovery of the affair with Véronique. Madame Brière, half-mad from fever, "hallucinated" from her bed, "Horrible things are going to happen in this house!" Thought to be out of danger, she suddenly died. The doctors were mystified, but not the citizens: she was "devoured by chagrins!"

Corancez is divided: "It's nothing but gossip, completely made up. I'd put my head under the knife for him. I've never seen him with a woman!" After his wife's death Brière "was not a father, he was a true *mother* to his kids. He took them to school, followed their progress with interest. The Sunday before the murders he had them fitted for new clothes for Béatrice's first communion! It's impossible that he committed these crimes against them!"

The widower wanted to remarry. He proposed to his mistresses. All refused. Véronique, coarse and ugly, had a father with beautiful fields. "I'll never marry a man with six children," she said. "Marry him, and you'll be eating dry bread!" said her father.

* * *

The court reporter from *Le Figaro* is searching for a motive: "The idea sprouted and developed while he led his plow into the great plain behind his house, and the sun made the lacy points of the cathedral golden from afar. His threshing business was going badly. The moment was coming when he'd have to sell his fields. His children were costing him a lot. They started to seem like sources of irritation. For me there's a strong resemblance between this crime, which gives us the shivers, and the fairy tales our mothers told us in our cribs."

He also quotes a magistrate from Chartres: "You can't judge this case like sentimental Parisians who when they're in the country are afraid to kill the chickens they've fed! Brière's not a worker from Belleville or Grenelle, he's a peasant from La Beauce, rude, energetic, and above all, hard. When he feels a need, he doesn't care what he has to do to satisfy it; that's typical of our region."

* * *

Corancez has only one casket sheet. A bed sheet is thrown over the other four and covered with wreaths and spring bouquets of field flowers. People file through the house using branches of boxwood to sprinkle the coffins with holy water. The town isn't rich, but it pays for the funeral.

Under a sky of startling purity, birds chirp in trees of new green. Sunlight inundates 500 mourners. Laurent's playmates lead the procession, bearing his casket. Some hold a banner lettered in gold: "Saint Laurent and Saint Blaise, our patron saints, pray for us!" A group of girls, friends of Flora, Béatrice, Laure, and Célina, carry a banner of the *Enfants de Marie*. Village women bear these coffins, followed by all the notables of the region, including Brière's relatives and Germaine, wearing a blue dress, draped with black. The church is hung with black cloth, trimmed in silver lamé. The mourners sing, beat drums, sound trumpets. Brière is forbidden to join them.

* * *

22 May 1901

My very dear papa

I wish sincerely that the truth about this horrible affair will soon be known, and we'll be delivered from the anguish that tortures us. I pray to God for you, dear papa, hoping He will hear an afflicted child. My aunt joins me in kissing you. Receive the assurance of my affectionate and devoted feelings,

Your daughter who loves you,

Germaine Brière

After reading this letter Brière cried for the first time. He responded with a father's heavy heart.

5 June 1901

My dear girl

I'm late in answering your letter. I'm very tired. No appetite for two or three days. This morning I got some food down. I believe I'll get better. I sleep very little. Endless nightmares.

What torments me most are thoughts of my little Célina, who didn't even attend school, who played near me with the doll you sent her. She'd not yet spoiled it. Ten times a day, she put it to sleep, always speaking of you. Poor little darling. Flora also spoke often of you, saying she wanted so much to see you behind the counter of the shop. I'd promised her she could visit you in Paris in September. Béatrice, Laurent, and Laure were happy to say, 'Marraine will come! She'll bring us bonbons!' Poor little darlings.

I end my letter embracing you with all my heart.

Your father Ed. Brière

10 June 1901

My dear papa

You speak of our little family whom you loved dearly. You gave yourself so much hardship for us! I think of the times you finished your day outside. In the evening you'd return, finding it completely natural to work in the house without a sound or spend half your nights caring for those who were sick. But now I see you've given yourself so much unhappiness! I'm sick at heart thinking about it, seeing you accused of such a crime. In my prayers I say to Flora, 'Speak to me, dear sister, you who have seen and know the guilty one.' From the sky I hear her say to me, 'Defend our unfortunate papa ... with all your heart, with all

BRIÈRE, CRIME OF CORANCEZ

Night of 21 – 22 April 1901

your strength. He is innocent!' Take good care of yourself, my dear papa, so that you can return in good health.

I kiss you a thousand times, and my aunt sends you a thousand kisses too. Your daughter who loves you,

Germaine Brière

The sentimental correspondence between father and daughter continues to produce the effect of the suspect as victim. But *Le Petit Journal* reproduces Brière's handwriting from one of these letters for amateur graphologists to analyze. Noting that nearly every word begins with a capital letter, the press sees someone "uneducated, with passionate appetites and a prideful spirit." In sum: a violent, combative egoist.

His fields haven't been cut. "No one in Corancez wants to touch the fields of a murderer, and since no one wants to rent his farm, it would be better to demolish it," sneers a reporter. Brière hopes he'll soon be freed. He writes his brother to cut the rye and alfalfa.

* * *

At the trial Brière's closely shaven face looks blue. Wearing the weeds of a widower, he assumes a spiritual expression. Members of the press are reminded of the man servant of a manor house or a chorus member from the Opéra-Comique until he is asked to put on the clothes he wore the night of the crime. Preserved for months, these specimens, bearing his children's blood and brains, restore his appearance to that of a butcher.

For a year, science has been able to distinguish human blood from that of other animals, but specialists from Paris can't agree about the red marks on Brière's shirt and jacket: "They're the blood of some beast or other." As for the ink on his fingers: "It resembled that in the bottle, but we can't verify it." Véronique testifies in low, confused whispers, bizarre in a hat trimmed with black feathers and water-green cabbage bows. Reporters titter. Brière killed for this freak? Germaine sobs. Pleading on her knees she makes two jurors weep. The judges cut short the "sadly useless" scene. Comby, Brière's defender from the Paris bar, delivers a summation in "delirious" phrases. The jury returns in six hours. "No extenuating circumstances. It's death!"

* * *

Brière's sentence was commuted to forced labor for life. A commission on criminal affairs and pardons reviewed his case, based on steps taken by the Leagues of the Rights of Man and of Individual Liberty. Justice makes mistakes, they said.

Before his departure to the penal colony Brière wrote "My innocence will be recognized. I'll soon be back among you. I'm an honest man! Ask the citizens of Corancez!"

But these citizens were furious. To them Brière's crime lay not in killing his children but in broadcasting Corancez's petty rivalries, miseries, and vices to the world, and worse, to their neighboring villages. As the rustics of La Beauce passed through the courtroom in dark blue blouses or white caps, testifying in the local patois, they were made to seem "a little stupid." Véronique Lubin, the scarecrow, forever sullied by the publicity, insisted Brière never asked to marry her: "Everything on that subject is a complete fabrication!" Her father, believed to be rich with property, but forced under oath to reveal he owned but a few acres, called Brière "the greatest criminal of the century."

20 Cherries in Syrup

1 February 1902, 10 Rue Elzévirs,
Raincy Pavillons, Bondy, northeast of Paris,
Arthur-Alexandre-Félix Leroy, 52, gardener,
murdered with hammer blows and four pistol
shots to the head by Edmond Bidaud, 26,
former railroad worker and his accomplice
Lucie-Antoinette Leboulleux, 22, prostitute.
Bidaud was sentenced to death. Sentence
commuted to forced labor for life.
Leboulleux sentenced to five years in prison.

A man's nothing but a stiff dick waiting to get it off. That's all they've ever been to me. They spill their seed. Then bye-bye. I never knew my old man. Mama don't neither. Men're what you use to get you money. Right? I tell them what they want to hear. So they feel good. Just for a while. They're gone soon enough.

Mama made it real clear I was a stone in her shoe. She did laundry to keep us fed. I'm grown, and she says, "You're bleeding my guts. Get your own bread." She puts me on the streets. A meal ticket's what she used me for. Merchandise up for sale.

I didn't like it one bit. Not her doing what she did. Throwing me out. But I don't hold no grudge. Dressing up to look smart for the men. That's what I hated. Hanging around in the dark. Trying to seem interested in what was passing by.

Pimps got me organized. But I had to work hard to feed them and keep mama living a life of ease. I lived separate, with an Alphonse, or by myself, depending. But I paid all her bills. I don't know if she was grateful. I don't even care. The money I got never seemed enough for what I had to do to get it. It hurt being with so many men. All of them pigs. Sweat or perfume. Was the same man-stink to me.

Worse though, I didn't have a friend in the world. Pimps are family, but they ain't friends. You're supposed to belly up for them so they'll protect you, but they cut you with their fists. I acted tough, puffed up myself with all the filth that came out of my mouth. I talk a good game. But there's no one who knows my real feelings. Never will.

I figured the chumps owed me a lot more than they were paying up front. So I sneaked a few bills while they put themselves back together. One got mad and had me arrested. The *flics* found out I was only fourteen. Mama got thrown in prison. Two years for corrupting a minor. That's what they said. Me, I got sent to a house of correction in Limoges to live with the sisters of Sainte-Madeleine till I came of age.

The mother superior was shocked at my foul mouth. But all of us in there talked dirty. "It's impossible to remake natures so prematurely depraved." That's what she told the *flics*. "These children are ignorant of nothing in life." Proves I was educated, right?

Seven years with the holy hens wasn't bad. There was piles to eat. They stuffed us with garbage about the Good Lord loving the weak best of all, and Jesus dying for our sins, but I made lots of friends. That's where I found out what true love feelings are like. Not the Good-Lord kind. Me and the others were all whores and thieves. Kids we were. Couldn't even wipe our own butts. We crawled in bed together to keep warm when the wood rations ran out. Men never held you close. Smoothed your hair. Or made you tickle.

In the convent I was a happy little chicken with a happy twat. Mother superior called my love for girls a "nervous malady." That's what produced my "cerebral derangements," she said. I don't understand. I'm no crazier than anyone who has my life. Getting back to the curbs I always had a girlfriend or two, for security.

Yvonne's a whore like me. We walk Montmartre with our arms around each other's waists in a lovers' knot. We go to the Rat Mort cabaret or the Quat'z'Arts and dance together. We stop and give each other long kisses. You can do that without anyone blinking at La Souris, or the Harcourt where women gather, or Le Hanneton where Madame Armande watches over us with the only eye she's got left. Yvonne loves me. Knows me better than anyone.

The Universal Exhibition saved my ass. Crowds of tourists wanting to get laid. I'm strolling outside the Palace of Electricity, and I meet this really sweet kid. Came to Paris from Chicago to work at the American pavilion. Paul Tackwell. Right off we started living like man and wife. He had to go home when the exhibition closed. I cried and cried. He was nice. "Maybe I'll see you in America some day." That's what I said. He said he really hoped so.

I wasn't looking for a man to take his place. I wasn't looking for a man to mean anything but pocket change. I had a room on the Rue de Beaujolais for customers. Doing fine. But this other guy shows up, and I went with him. He was a singer in the music halls. Ducassou. A smooth talker. Edmond Bidaud was his real name. I wasn't exactly his type. He was good looking and well brought up. Pince-nez and fancy talk. Double talk, it seemed to me. I'm a street kid. I been used hard. Twenty-one, and I already got a double chin!

"You like to help me out?" That's what Edmond said. I'm thinking there might be less whoring to do if I go along with his game. Me and him didn't screw much. He was too busy dreaming up the next move. His sex feeling traveled from his cock and got stuck in his head. Had nothing to do with me. That's what he said. He used to get excited watching me and Yvonne getting it off. I think he got us occupied so he could steal from our pocketbooks. I caught on soon enough. I had a hell of a lot to do keeping up with his schemes.

With Edmond I mostly gave up cunt to tell lies. Some work, me acting the sweet young thing, or his bride, depending. "We're in Paris on our honeymoon," he'd tell whoever he had a mind to swindle. We were in and out of furnished hotels all over Paris and Versailles, paying for rooms with cheap jewelry I'd pull off my fingers. Skipping before they saw the stuff wasn't worth forty sous. Him with a false beard. Me in my persian lamb bolero, flaunting respectable airs. I liked it right off.

Women stuck to Edmond like maggots on meat. He spoke in the familiar to old ladies, maids. Didn't matter. I had my own reasons for sticking. The fewer dicks the better was how I saw it.

He took up with Madame Mésnard long before I came along. She was seventy-five. Nuts about him. She made him screw her a lot. He figured he deserved her pickings for how tired he got. Kids where she lived made jokes about the dizzy old coquette with a dandy twenty-six in love with her. Edmond got more than 10,000 francs off granny Mésnard. He had a legitimate wife, Blanche Poisson. He brought her round to Madame Mésnard's. The old lady didn't care. He kept them both satisfied.

Edmond using me was a nice living. He'd get a new idea, and we'd chase after that. But suddenly old lady Mésnard dies, and Edmond gets morose. I don't know if it was his money bag drying up or what. But one day, he says, "There's an old friend I used to know when I was a kid. Gardener. Name of Leroy. He lives near the Bondy Forest. My father owes him 400 francs from years back. It's time I repaid the loan. Wanna come along as my wife?"

So I play Madame Bidaud. We visit the gardener. Edmond says we're happily married. Rich too. To make the guy think we weren't after anything of his. "We want to share our happiness with our long lost friends." That's what he says. He pays the gardener the old loan. Nice outlay for greater gains to come. That's how he saw it. And wasn't the old boy delighted? Smiling like sunshine, he slipped the francs in his pocket.

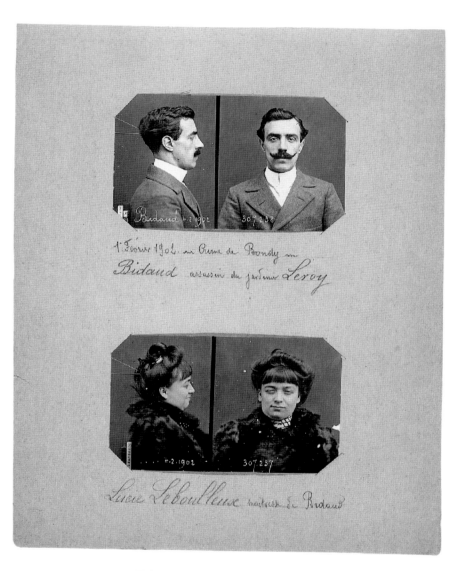

1ᵉʳ Février 1902 un Crime de Bondy un
Bidaud assassin du jardinier Leroy

Lucie Leboulleux maitresse de Bidaud

I FEBRUARY 1902, CRIME OF BONDY

Bidaud, murderer of the gardener Leroy
Lucie Leboulleux, Bidaud's mistress

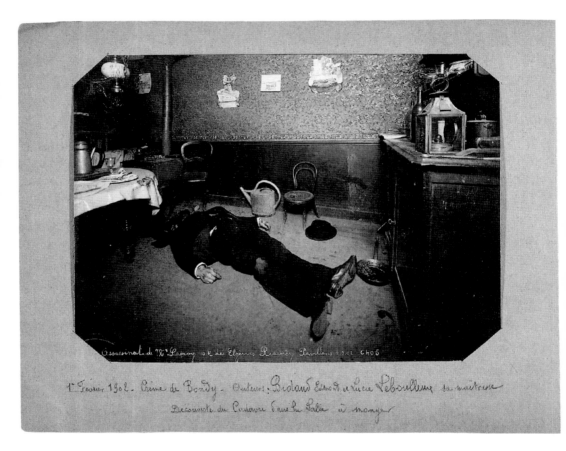

MURDER OF MONSIEUR LEROY, 10 RUE DES ELZÉVIRS, RAINCY PAVILLONS, 2. 2. 02

1 February 1902, crime of Bondy, committed by:

Bidaud, Edmond and Lucie Leboulleux, his mistress

Discovery of the body in the dining room

Crime de Bondy — Vue de la maison de la Victime

MURDER OF MONSIEUR LEROY, 10 RUE DES ELZÉVIRS, RAINCY PAVILLONS, 2. 2. 02

Crime of Bondy: view of the house of the victim

The gardener's doing well too. "I saved 5,000 francs to build a new house." That's what he says. We're drinking wine.

"Isn't it dangerous to keep your money at home?" That's what Edmond says.

"Oh no. I've got it hidden in the attic."

I'm laughing to myself.

We try to keep the friendship going. We write the gardener on stationery Edmond stole from the Café Cardinale on the Boulevard des Italiens. "Monsieur, would you and Madame Leroy care to join me and my wife for lunch on the Avenue de l'Opéra?" Something must've looked fishy because we wrote twice, but the gardener never wrote back. Edmond says, let's go to Bondy and surprise him.

I've sucked off hundreds of dopes like Leroy. Regular types. Hungry for it on the sneak. Fuck whores day and night if they could. The gardener's wife wrinkles her puss like I smell bad. When her back's turned I steal the oranges from a bowl on the table. I take three new handkerchiefs off the ironing board. Leroy gives me a wicked smile.

He's married fifteen years. Perfect husband and father. That's what his neighbors think. He's not the type to take up with an easy woman. Ha! Ain't my experience. I look at him sly, like I got something sweet on my tongue I want him to taste. His dick's getting hard. He buttons his jacket. Which looks comical when you're home in your own dining room. He takes us aside. "Come when Madame Leroy's at work in Paris and our son's at school." That's what he says. "If your wife spent some agreeable moments with me, I could make her very happy." Edmond pretends he's heard a joke. I think we're making progress.

Edmond says I should visit the gardener myself. I follow orders. Me and Leroy have a couple of stupid conversations. I know he wants relations, but he's afraid to propose anything direct. I come back again. Edmond waits in a bar in Noisy-le-Sec. I tell Leroy, "Edmond's pissing away my dowry." The old boy gives me 140 francs, just to be nice, but it's not what we have in mind.

Again we come back. I go in. Edmond waits in the cold. Leroy's dressed up, on his way out. He looks glad to see me anyhow. He pours some wine. There's cherries in syrup in a jar on the table, and cheese and bread for our *tête-à-tête*. I have on my red dress. Before I know it, he's on his knees. His hand's fishing under my skirts. I'm staring at the garnet in his tie pin.

Who does he see through the dining room window? Edmond! I do my best shriek of horror. Edmond flies in. "You're taking advantage of my wife! Are you trying to injure me, Monsieur?" Edmond's all worked up. "You've forced me to take revenge!" Leroy's got me by the neck. Edmond said later the guy was trying to kiss me. That wasn't it. Leroy was scared stiff, holding on to me for dear life. Crapping his pants. "My husband's dangerous when he's jealous!" That's what I yell and run to the garden, which is why there was no blood on my dress.

Inside Edmond's playing the cuckold. He busts Leroy's skull with a pressing iron he grabs off the stove. Blood's all over the dining room. "The gardener tried to shoot me. I had to protect myself!" That's what he tells the *flics*. But it was an air gun for killing tree sparrows in the garden. Couldn't do no damage on a person. Besides Leroy was half-dead from what Edmond did to him with the iron. How could he stand up and shoot? Edmond pulls out a revolver and puts four bullets in his head. To defend himself from the poor corpse! I'm laughing just thinking about it.

Edmond empties Leroy's wallet. He rifles the whole house. Savings from a sugar bowl, set of keys, Madame Leroy's ring. I'm shivering outside. It's rotten cold. Edmond's taking too long. The houses are close together out here. I'm a target in red against the snow. Everyone can see me. I'm thinking Edmond must be working the attic. He comes out.

"We gotta leave," I say.

"All right! I searched upstairs. Just a trunk with old papers. There's no 5,000 francs there." It was under a floorboard. That came out at the trial.

When they caught us, filth flew out my mouth. I acted the snoot. "Don't touch me. You'll get me dirty!" That's what I told my guard. Butter wouldn't melt in my mouth. That's what he said. They thought I was insane, especially after what the mother superior told them about me and the girls in the convent.

They photographed me at the prefecture. I played it like a comedy. It was. Me standing in bare feet, being measured and handled by police. Worse than customers. I winced and blinked when they made my picture. I was grinning like a monkey. They put me like that in the permanent records and the newspapers. I wonder what Yvonne thought. The papers said I was a coquette. "But those who know her from this picture will not keep the memory of a pretty woman." Pigs. They'll never know me.

They wanted a sample of my handwriting. To see if it was me who wrote the letter to Leroy asking him to lunch. "Write," says the judge. He starts dictating:

"Dear papa," he says.

I start laughing. "I ain't writing that! Papa! Who the fuck's papa? Do you know my father? If so, kindly give my mother the information. She'd be ever so grateful." The judge and the lawyers said my situation was grave. They meant, cut the jokes.

They found my blue collar in a trunk I left in Versailles. "I want it back. It flatters my coloring!" That's what I said. They found my black dress. "Oh good," I said. "I'm sick of my red one. I've worn it so much. I need a change of clothes. Saint-Lazare uniform don't keep me warm enough." It's the truth. Coldest winter I could remember.

Edmond's real wife Blanche took the stand at the trial, all in black. Like someone died. She cried looking at me. "She's not even pretty!" She says that to Edmond. "I thought you had better taste! You'll be condemned to death. I won't see you anymore. One less reason to hate you!" I guess she felt good getting it off her chest. Edmond was embarrassed. He tells the jury. "Please pardon my wife."

What did that mean? He's the one who should be hoping for a pardon!

My lawyer told stories about me. "Lucie was just a tool, an instrument of men's rude pleasures." Hearing that, I bawled like I was at the melodrama. Rolled around on the floor. I didn't know how sad my life was till he got hold of it. They thought I was faking a nervous crisis, but I wasn't. He made it sound like I was really in love with Edmond. That I attached myself to him as he had to me. My lawyer was thinking about the can of sardines I gave Edmond. I got it from the prison. He said he was hungry. "Here have this little bite," I said. He ate it right up! It didn't mean I was his true love. My lawyer made me look good. That's when he said I had no blood on my clothes when the gardener's room was covered with it. So I must be innocent. Right?

I heard that when they went to see Edmond's father, the old man took his photograph off the wall. "I want to forget him. Take this." He pulled the picture out of the frame and tore it up. "But he was just a child!" That's what his mama was crying. I wonder if my mama'd cry like that for me. I don't know where she is. I'll have to look a long time. Bet she's in America, old bitch.

21 La Petite Gourmet

3 March 1902, 80 Rue Caulaincourt,
XVIIIth Arrondissement, Angèle Chèze, 7,
living at 76 Rue Lamarck, suffocated to death
by Henri-Guillaume-Hector Ducocq,
called Masson, 32, coachman, pimp. Ducocq,
a Belgian citizen, was arrested in Brussels,
tried there, and sentenced to forced labor for
life. In Montmartre, before the crime, illustrator
Théophile-Alexandre Steinlen gave him a cat.

Sunday morning, early March, I'm out drawing cats for a poster on milk. I've got plenty of felines at home, but those little darlings bored me. I needed street cats. Mean ones with secrets. I put a hisser in a poster for Salis's Chat Noir cabaret. His back was up, practically shooting sparks. I made him an icon, black, and byzantine. Framed the head with a red halo. Lettered it, *Mon Joye Montmartre.*

Montmartre was Salis's spiritual home. Mine as well. I avoid the center of Paris. Too many rich bastards. I prefer country mud and windmills. I took Lautrec's old studio on the Rue Caulaincourt, but I then got a better place at number 80. Renoir's a few doors down. He takes his rheumatism south in the cold months. I stay put. I'll die in Montmartre, with the broken-down coach drivers, laborers, whores and pimps, lechers who follow girls loaded with laundry. They're my people. I draw them large and strong, fierce and clear.

Depravity's wide open in the music halls up here. I drew the fat necks gawking at frenetic cancans on stage. I put these bourgeois into the satirical newspapers. Anarchy's in every line I make. Perfect with Aristide Bruant's poetry. We're carnivores when it comes to the crowd. I helped decorate Bruant's cabaret Le Mirliton. I drew him standing on a table, like a roaring bull, calling his audience a bunch of abortions. He wore that phrase out. Women were at his feet, smiling like he drugged them, practically peeing in their pantaloons from his taunts. On city walls my designs are wonderful. They dramatize the struggles of the people who appreciate my sad laughter. I won't labor the matter, but I'm another one who thinks Dreyfus is being framed.

Other celebrities besides Bruant seek me out. Yvette Guilbert chose my poster over Lautrec's for her '94–'95 season at the Ambassadeurs. He's the better artist. But he made her look so ugly. I drew her skinny, the fashion for her kind of performer. I also showed her as the great song-sayer she is.

Wherever I go, the city's a drama. I see what others ignore. Starving painters with mistresses spitting blood at the Cabaret des Arts, sniffing mongrels mounting each other, concierges, men pretending to study shop windows, waiting, sometimes stalking a child.

Sunday morning at eight, street cats were everywhere, the way I like them, wild, spitting, weaving in and out of the mist. They're the artists Loïe Fuller tries to imitate when she twirls her veils at the Folies-Bergère. I caught the line of a cat's back with my crayon, curved tail, wicked points of the ears, its streaked pounce from curb to cobblestones, alert for the threat of carriages.

The air was cold. I was content, thinking the children would soon leave their breakfasts to come and watch. Angèle Chèze, she's seven, will pester, ask more questions than I can answer. She's intelligent. Already reads. Besides, she has a wonderful cat, Cassis, which she brought to my table. I sketched them both.

I observe. I don't interfere. I see what mothers don't when they send their kids on errands to the butcher or for a loaf of bread. I watch men in cloth slippers offer candy and coax them to take their hand. Mothers gazing from windows at the shacks and empty lots are dreaming of a shining future in the city below. They don't suspect their babies know these drifters. A good mother wouldn't think of letting her kids wander into a dark wood. But there's no darker wood than the streets of Paris. The children don't tell mama because something about the men feels gentle, also dangerous and exciting. The little gluttons are tempted by the candy and stuff their pockets. I'm drawing. I look up as the man reaches for them. "Come along," he says. They run away. I continue drawing.

I saw a calico circling a brindled black. Beautiful color. Through the fog the figure of a little girl moved along the Rue Lamarck toward the Rue Damremont. Angèle Chèze. She's a pious silhouette in her hooded brown cape. I sketched the delicate triangle she made.

She passes where the Rue Lamarck crosses my street. A man in a fur-lined cloak stepped forward. Masson. I'm surprised, him out so early. He usually waits till dusk to eat at Alexandre's open-air bar. Masson's not his real name. Probably not Parisian either. I'm a foreigner myself so I notice accents. There's a touch of Belgian in his French. He lives behind my building with Blanche who whores for him on the Boulevard de Clichy. She's gone to Nice for a couple of weeks to let some mess with a client blow over. Masson's alone. Masson always had a lot of free time. He watched me draw and asked why I cared so much about cats. He bragged about his black poodle. "Dogs are too anxious to please," I said. "Cats teach you with their silence"—when it comes to these beautiful beasts, I'm a philosopher. Next time he showed up I had him wait on the sidewalk while I ran to my studio. I came back with a pink female and put it in his arms.

"I have so many. This one's pretty. You'll see what I mean." He was pleased. "I'll take good care of her." He attracts kids. He's one I watch who gives them candy.

I've seen Angèle talk with Masson, like he's an old friend. Today she passed, but he doesn't speak to her. She seemed not to notice him.

She's intent on her errand: "I won't eat my Sunday bread and butter if Cassis doesn't have something good to eat too. Papa gave me a sou. I'm going to the tripe shop to buy my cat some tasty innards." She smiles, clutching her basket. I smile back.

It's eight-thirty. Cats are piling up in my notebook. The street's empty except for the lines they make in the fog. I saw a man running, panting. Angèle's papa.

"You seen her?"

"She's getting tripe for Cassis."

"That takes ten minutes. She's been gone much too long. Watch for her, will you?"

This father'll go to the tripe shop, then to the police, who'll reassure him. They get loads of reports on lost kids. The little truants return in a few hours, without a care. Chèze passed me again.

"I had them telegraph all the police stations in the city. She's gone, Monsieur."

I stuffed my notebook in my pocket. The fog didn't gobble her up. I'd seen her. And Masson watching. I didn't tell the father. He's excitable. I'm Swiss. I stay calm, though if my little daughter Colette disappeared in the mist I'd be a crazy man. I walked down the Rue Lamarck to the tripe shop on the Rue Damremont. "Like I told her father, I watched when she left, but then I had to serve a customer."

"She go back toward her street?"

"No. Turned right."

I walked, trying to trace her path, taking the Rue Tourlaque to the Rue Lepic. The arms of the Moulin de la Galette loomed overhead. I couldn't see a meter ahead of me. I passed a wooden box with five legs — an old actor photographing under a dark cloth. He combs the Rue des Saules and the Rue Mont-Cenis looking for shacks, trees and street vendors. Like I do cats. I saw him shoot a lamp-shade seller on the Rue Lepic. My kind of subject. "They're disappearing," he told me. "You can blame the department stores."

"Did you see a little girl?"

Rue des Saules où est deumant le cadavre.

Ducoq, Hector, dit Masson.

Angèle Chèze.

DUCOQ, HECTOR, CALLED MASSON

Rue des Saules where the body was discovered; Angèle Chèze

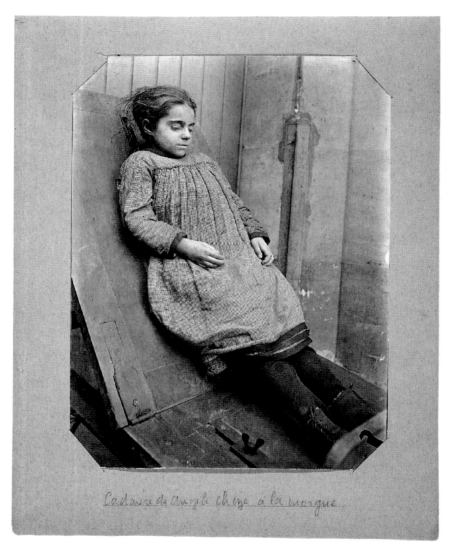

Cadavre de Angèle chèze à la morgue

BODY OF ANGÈLE CHÈZE AT THE MORGUE

Cadavre de la petite Angèle Chèze

BODY OF LITTLE ANGÈLE CHÈZE

"Nobody's out this hour on Sundays. The fog's perfect. Today'll be one of my good days. I have to get this clump of buildings before the sun breaks through and hard shadows take over."

I didn't have time for his picturesque theories. I hurried along the Rue Norvins. Two little boys were walking near a school.

"Have you seen Angèle Chèze?"

"She's with a man. Her hood was up, but we recognized her. We wanted to tell her a joke, but she had her nose in the air."

"Was she crying? Trying to get away?"

"No. Just walking."

"The man?"

"He gives us candy. He was carrying her basket. After they passed, he dropped it in the gutter."

I ran up the Rue des Saules. In the distance, a man and a little girl. I started to tremble. He's leading her to his shanty. She's clever. Why doesn't she run? Should I think he's up to something evil? I gave this pervert one of my prettiest cats! I could have met them face to face, struck up a conversation so she could slip off. I could have led her home. I was afraid. I didn't know what to do. I went back to my studio and sketched them from memory.

Monday night, around ten-thirty, I'm drinking wine with some artists on the Rue des Saules. The street's black but for the lamps of the bar. Suddenly Charles Pelletier, a kid, a policeman's son, storms in. Face white. Teeth chattering. He says follow me to number 29. Coming home and turning the key, he noticed a large package. Curious, he bent to touch the wrapping. A wool cape. He poked around — a warm body.

We ran to where he led. We cut the cords, pushed away the cloth. Angèle. Serene, almost smiling. A jute cord, like a clothes line, tight around her neck, holding her bent legs and arms behind her back. Her father was searching for two days, and here we find her. She seemed to be breathing. We carried her to the bar and called a doctor. He arrived to declare her officially dead.

Two days since I last saw her, and I did nothing. I'm an artist, not the police. I despise their meddling. This was different, a little girl I knew with a cat. Her father was frantic, showing everyone a photograph of her at five, smiling in a white dress. His only daughter. No one'd seen her. He complained the cops didn't start searching till Monday when it was too late. His wife was already sick, but when Angèle disappeared she took to her bed. Chèze'd been to the station on the Impasse Tourlaque a hundred times. Now he came to make a positive identification. He saw Angèle's calm expression and fell to his knees. "She's only sleeping! Wake up, *ma petite*!" He sobbed and folded her in his arms. He waited to tell his wife. She was in a dangerous state of collapse.

Angèle's dead. No one knows where Masson is. I watch. I record. I don't butt in. I saw them. I could have stopped it. I crossed a court-yard and passed Madame Maugars, Masson's neighbor, standing out-side her shanty.

"I already talked. Chief Cochefert's been here all night with twenty agents. Swarming rats, they were. You with them?"

"I'm with the newspapers." I didn't say they were the kind that make people laugh.

"Like I told them, eight-thirty Sunday morning, I'm with my little girl and her mutt. Out the window I see Masson. Cloak spread out, hiding something. His dog yanks the chain. Starts barking terrible. A little girl jumps free. I seen her clear. Wouldn't take another step, fearful of the dog, she was. Masson shoos the animal away. Yells, 'Go on now!' Then they go to his room.

"Later, I seen him in shirt sleeves going to the water closets. Next he's in the courtyard. Cutting down laundress Thironet's clothes line. Later I meet him on the stairs leading to our shanties. He's got two packages. I'm not mistaken. One was sweets.

"Late next day he knocks. 'Got a little soused,' he says. 'Com-mitted a nasty folly.' I didn't catch his meaning. Says he's leaving. Would I feed his dog and cat? I says sure. Now I'm thinking me safe at home and all the while him in there snuffing out the little girl." She puts an arm around her daughter and the mutt.

Outside Masson's shanty, agents are digging in a big pit. They think he buried the baby his whore Blanche bore him there, that they didn't send it to public assistance as she claimed. Nothing suspicious is turning up. I tell the guard I'm a reporter. He waves me inside.

Monsieur Bertillon's set up his camera in the miserable hole Masson and Blanche had for ten francs a month. He's exploding flash powder off the walls papered with pages from sporting newspapers. He's getting the mahogany bed, filthy sheets, coverlet of torn women's dresses, washbowl, broken mirror, cast-iron stove, rotten table and chairs, red-lined coat and lace-trimmed pantaloons on a nail. I'm thinking they're the last things Angèle saw.

Cochefert's excited. The clothesline Masson cut down in the courtyard matches cords that tied the child. He wraps two tea cups in a handkerchief. One shows a chalky residue. "He gave her something to drink. Probably a narcotic. A vial on the table smells of ether. That's why the neighbors didn't hear any crying."

Agents are emptying a steamer trunk of men's clothes. They find photographs. "That's him," I say. Masson's posed outdoors near a drainpipe. He's wearing an imperial mustache and pointed beard. Height of elegance twenty-five years ago, they sit on his face like deformities. He has no collar. His rumpled jacket's closed tight. A buttonhole has a fresh flower. His hat's a fancy grey fedora. Vain pleasure sneaks past his lips. His eyes hold sensual reveries. "Boulevard gallant gone to seed," say the agents. Street cat, I tell myself. Bertillon takes the snapshot for his files.

Dr Socquet, the police physician, examines Angèle's body. She wasn't raped. "No violence of any kind." What did Masson want? To take tea and cakes with a lively little girl and tie her up? It's not the first time.

Cochefert checks the records. Four years ago, Masson lured a little girl of eight to his room on the Rue Voltaire, molested her, bound her with cord, then set her free. Her parents denounced him to the police who brought him to the station. But they had to let him go. When a kid's taken and returned unharmed the law says there's no crime. After theft, molesting girls is the commonest crime in Paris. Most people are too ashamed to report it, but known cases number 30,000 a year. Masson had his fun. This time he went a little further.

Socquet analyzes Angèle's stomach. It's empty. Any cakes she ate in the shanty were digested when she died. I'm thinking maybe there was no tea party. As Masson's prisoner, maybe she didn't eat anything at all.

Bertillon goes to the Rue des Saules and photographs the doorway where we found her. I join the crowd, cordoned off so he can make his pictures. We make a black band at the foot of the stairs. Bertillon asks Lucie Mobailly, a nine-year-old at the same address, to be Angèle for the shot. She lies in the street wrapped in a cape. Everyone wants a part in these murders. Lucie plays dead on a street where the Cabaret des Assassins used to be. Its walls were decorated with pictures of Troppmann's sensational killing, thirty years back, of a mother and her five kids. Crime is manna in this quarter.

I knew it. Masson's Belgian. Real name: Hector Ducocq. Cochefert's positive he's fled France. The previous arrest for molesting doesn't count. He has another reason to hide. He got ten years of solitary with hard labor for stealing 4,500 francs when he worked at the central markets. But he disappeared before they could make him serve. I saw him skulking. He was hiding from something big like that.

Cochefert always gets strange postcards and notes signed by crack-pots with phoney confessions. But one from the Grand Duchy of Luxembourg smells genuine: "I'm Hector Ducocq, presumed murderer of the little girl in Montmartre. I fled so as not to serve ten years for theft, but I didn't kill the little girl. I'm with a good friend. You'll never lay a hand on me." That's it. Play up the lesser crime. Throw them off the scent of the worse one.

The police find Ducocq in Brussels. He's living with *La Boule,* a mulatto, former gymnast at the Hippodrome at the end of my street. Ducocq, dressed in black, recut his goatee and the points of his mustache. All he had was a franc and some centimes. They said he shook like a leaf.

I was with the 10,000 who followed Angèle's coffin to the cemetery. She was our child. We shouted our rage, from the morgue to the church in Jules-Joffrin Square. Her bier was covered with wreathes and bouquets from the tripe shop, from Gallet & Company where her father is a teller, from tenants in her building, and school children of Montmartre. Her mother, flanked by relatives, rode in a hackney cab. "I'll poke his eyes out! He took my girl!" The parents had to fight to get a seat in the church.

Children and girls from a boarding school, directed by Angèle's aunt, led the procession. "Without exaggeration," the newspapers said, "two hundred thousand blackened the Rue Mont-Cenis and the Boulevard Ornano to pay homage." The papers weren't lying. I was there. It was dark before the custodians of Saint-Ouen cemetery pushed out all the mourners.

"She was a greedy little thing," Angèle's aunt told Cochefert. Mean-spirited shame, I thought. The aunt runs a school for girls. She's trying to teach her charges more important things than temptations of cake and candy. But her niece fell into the pit. "Greedy" doesn't explain my *petite gourmet* or the power of her hypnotist.

Cassis won't eat. He calls for her. Throws himself at the door when he hears a child on the stairs. Madame Chèze wails. Does this mama curse the creature's love of tripe? Will she fling him out as a wretched reminder of her lost girl? I'll watch. If he's on the streets, cold and hungry, I swear, Angèle, I'll take him home.

22 The Panther

8 April 1902, 104 Rue du Faubourg
Saint-Antoine, XIIth Arrondissement,
Fernand-Marcel Legrand, 6,
decapitated with a razor by his stepfather,
Adrien-Virgile Legrand, 24, hairdresser's
assistant. Sentenced to forced labor
for life.

I came to see him everyday. His spots were faint rosettes against his black coat. They'd disappear and return again as he paced his filthy cage. I was breathless, weakened by this shape shifting in such a grand and terrifying creature. He was a vision in a dream, a phantom shade from the cinematographic theater.

At first he didn't like me staring. His roar, a raspy cough, alerted the attendant. "Stay clear! They kill for no reason — dogs, goats, even children!" That didn't mean me. I'd found a brother in this magnificent beast.

Life is full of wonderful coincidences. The Jardin des Plantes is near the Salpêtrière hospital where my wife is a nurse. It was easy to visit him without anyone suspecting. I started walking my wife to work. The attention delighted her. We'd only been married six months, and she'd written me off as a drunken good-for-nothing, though she was too polite to say so. She thought we looked stylish crossing the Seine on the Austerlitz Bridge.

When we reached the hospital, she pecked me on the cheek, and sent me home. Her little boy Fernand will be afraid if he wakes up and no one's there. After she disappeared behind the statue of Dr Pinel, I ran to the zoological gardens of the Jardin des Plantes. They don't open till eleven, but I slipped unnoticed through an opening near the Bear Pits. Past this braying hole, the elephants, and Frémiet's *Stone-Age Man,* I saw my panther.

My night hunter. One pounce, and he'll break your neck. Sometimes, he'd yawn to show me the cave of his mouth and throat. I'd push my face against the bars to inhale his breath. It bathed me in unearthly sweetness. I needed to feel his power against me. I pushed my umbrella through the bars to touch him. He stopped and took a special interest. I melted in his golden gaze. I'm a speck in that ocean. I don't care. He needs me. Wonderful dream! The morning mist rose over the lawns. The peonies were at their peak. The beds of medicinal plants refreshed the stinking cages that punish wild beasts, imprison them in forests of iron bars. With my wife safely at her job and Fernand asleep in his crib, I was right where I belonged.

One day, when I reached again to touch my brother, he crashed against the bars and in one swipe nearly tore off my arm. My blood flowed into the cage. He lapped it up. He would have finished me, but for the bars between us. His wish to devour me was a desire for union. He longed to embrace me the only way he could. My blood combined with the poisons from his talons. His secrets poured into me. My pain was sublime. I left the garden wondering what to tell my wife. I hugged my wounds and ran home.

Since that wonderful day I don't belong to Paris. He tasted my blood and welcomed me into his family. Not like me and my wife where I'm her flunky. Or at my job where I compliment the customers so they'll tip me for holding the hairpins. With my brother I'm an equal.

When my wife saw the panther's marks, she couldn't hide her astonishment. She dressed them gently and murmured sweet endear-

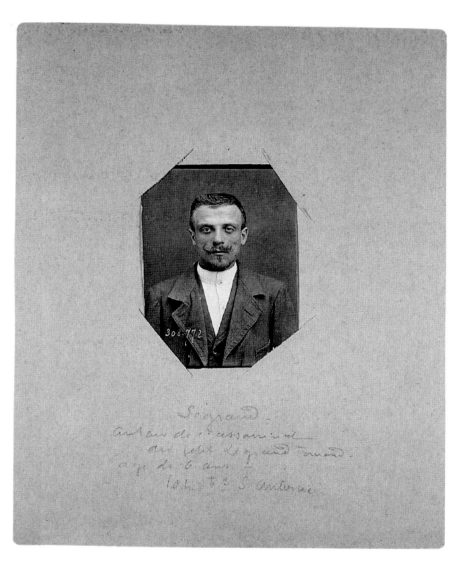

LEGRAND

Murderer of little Legrand, Fernand, age 6
104 Faubourg Saint-Antoine

ments. As I said, she's an excellent nurse. How could she understand the importance of my initiation? Could I expect her and all the people in my building to realize I was in a secret society, no longer a member of the human race?

At the Salpêtrière my wife takes care of hundreds of mad women. Another secret society. The doctors think they'll win their way into this circle and grasp its mysteries. They're doomed to fail. I understand the residents of the Salpêtrière. No one will cure them. They're there to fool the doctors, make them believe their science is important.

These women pretend to be actresses. My wife says special photographers come in to capture the different stages of their hysterical attacks. She says Sarah Bernhardt visits the hospital so she can steal these movements and play them in the real theater. Even Sarah-the-Divine needs to belong to something greater, more mysterious than herself.

As I do. I see my face in the mirror, and the two sides don't match. Look at my photograph. One side is the face of a failure, a hairdresser's lackey. The other side has the eye of a big cat. If you bother to look, you'll discover this difference in yourself. People are too frightened to look at anyone's face, much less their own.

My neighbors live like oysters on a rock, miserably dull. They pass me on the stairs. They gossip and think I don't notice. I try to live in a regular way, but my heart isn't in anything I do. I've done time for robbery. My happiest days were in a penal colony in Africa. There I discovered my interest in playing around with children. Even now, these preying influences take all my strength.

Back to my story. You'll see how important the details are in events which reached an astonishing conclusion and changed my life. One morning I left my wife at the hospital to help the doctors pursue the secrets of the mad women, who are really way above her and the doctors, way beyond the theories of that phoney hypnotist, Dr Charcot. Around six, I crossed the boulevard. When I got to the cage, it was empty. I wasn't surprised.

I watched for his massive head above the beds of medicinal plants. Maybe he was lounging in a tree, tearing apart some dog he grabbed off the boulevards. Or I might see his tail disappearing around a corner like a black satin ribbon. Of course, he'd stop and regard me with perfect trust.

I crossed the Austerlitz Bridge and entered the Rue du Faubourg Saint-Antoine through the Rue Traversière where I stopped at the laundry to collect two fresh sheets. I followed him to the bakery. His scent rose above the freshly baked bread. I bought a loaf. He led me to the grocer's. I bought a liter of wine. At my building, I walked softly past the concierge. Her black cat crossed my path and made a raspy cough. I climbed five flights to the mansard. Any moment I'd meet him, gazing down on the world, waiting for me to fulfill his mission.

Fernand was asleep. I hung my coat on a nail and removed his undershirt and chemise. He was naked, completely innocent. I placed the bread and wine on the table, unfolded one of the sheets and spread it over him. I opened my hairdresser's box of razors, scissors, and whetstone. I pulled out a blade. I raised the sheet over Fernand's head. Suddenly, he pushed his little fists through the bars of his crib! I flung myself against it, ran my claw across his throat. In a surge of animal power I sacrificed Fernand. My panther saw this and loved me.

Fernand wet himself. It smelled. His blood soaked the sheet. I wanted to vomit. My ears started ringing. Wind tore my clothing. I ran to my neighbor Monsieur Elie. "My wife's child died! In a terrible way!" Elie didn't believe me. I stayed downstairs while he ran up to look. Maybe he lifted the sheet and saw Fernand's severed head. He was screaming, pounding on all the neighbors' doors. My panther left his signature. Four bloody marks on the wall. Nobody identified the message but me.

My new life required drastic measures. The police found me sobbing. I told the chief detective "they" killed Fernand, but this walrus didn't understand. Three doctors came to examine the child and started whispering. They noticed other marks "of an odious nature" on him and decided he'd endured terrible suffering for some time. I thought big cats made quick kills. Was my brother with Fernand before the final moment? The police found my razors. One of the blades was damaged. I'm a beast when called upon.

I cried telling my wife who wasted no time in humiliating me. She let the police know I'd been under her watchful eye since the panther first claimed me. She said, in hospital language, I showed signs of "cerebral derangement." I told the police I killed Fernand. I didn't say he also joined our brotherhood. I told them what they'd understand. "I had a hallucination." They called me crazy and locked me up.

My wife's crazy too. Since they buried Fernand she lives at the Salpêtrière. I have a photograph of her. She's smiling and looks right at home. Her fingers spell out letters. With her left hand she's making a sinister sign. Nobody can tell me she hasn't crossed over to a secret society of her own. This opened us to terrible treacheries.

Which brings me to the last part of my story, which I hope you'll see correctly: soon after the police took me away, three robbers broke into our apartment, stole the bread, the remaining sheet, all of Fernand's clothes, and my razors. Why were these things still there? Don't the detectives take them as evidence? Or are they also crazy? The newspapers called the burglary "a weird coincidence." To the police the intruders looked like ordinary thieves. I don't think they behaved in an ordinary way. They sat at my table and opened the wine, which I forgot in the fury of events, and drank it all. They were honoring the scene of my ritual. Our network is vast.

23 Sisters

29 April 1902, 49 Avenue de Wagram,
XVIIth Arrondissement, Emilie-Alexandrine
Blanchet, Widow Laporte, 74, strangled
and robbed. Assailant unknown.

I'm nobody really, just Madame Quérilé, one of the maids who worked for Widow Laporte. We were all birds of passage. She never praised my services, but I must have done fine since she let me stay on. Besides, I learned something special about her. In the end it didn't matter what I knew. I lost my job like the rest.

The widow could afford to be fussy. Two dead husbands left her sitting on a pile. Monsieur Sauriac, the first, was mayor of Saint-Ouen. Then a businessman, Monsieur Laporte. She didn't spend any money as far as I could see. She just saved and saved. "Why give it over to the banks? They only use it like it's their own. Banks'll lead you to the poor house!" was her philosophy. Maybe she was right.

"And don't go fussing with my secretary. It's locked. Give me your cloth. I'll dust it, myself." That's where she sat, scheming and adding up figures. I imagined the stash hidden in the piece of furniture, seeping through the locks and hinges, yellow eyes following me while I swept and polished. It almost made me look forward to coming to work and putting up with her snippy comments.

Once I saw the hoard. In the bedroom. I was stripping the sheets. I flipped the mattress, and what showed up but piles of bank notes and gold and silver coins! More besides, in two leather sacks. I caught my breath. Old sneak! Cash warming her brittle bones!

I stared a long while. Like I was caught in a spell. I held up my apron, thinking I'd catch more falling from the sky. A louis or two might stick to my fingers. I could grab a fistful of bills. She wouldn't see. But I stopped myself. Just as well. I felt her dark shadow behind me. The old crow caught me dazzled by her money. A vision from the clouds!

"Leave that alone, nosy creature!" she shrieked, spoiling my dream. She pushed me into the hall. Later I saw her lock the sacks, one yellow, one black, in a cupboard. I don't know what she did with the rest. That's how she was, miserly and cunning.

The only amusement she had when I was around were her barometers. She liked to follow the weather's ups and downs. She wrote the numbers in a little diary and compared them with the numbers in the newspaper. "I keep better track than the professors," she bragged when all of Paris expected rain, but outside was a sunny day.

After I saw her fortune she started keeping track of me. Read me like I was one of her instruments. Tried to figure what I'd do if I thought she wasn't looking. They know when you're on the take. Better to resist temptation, is my philosophy. Count on their good graces. You get more in the end. Besides, if I was caught pinching, she'd have bounced me like the rest.

Widow Laporte and I had our routine. I'd arrive early from the suburbs, make her breakfast cocoa, and try to keep the place to her standards. I'd leave around one-thirty, after bringing in a midday meal from a restaurant. She had me eat with her to keep me in view so I wouldn't pilfer her commodes while she chewed her lamb chop. She didn't take dinner. She ate left overs from lunch.

They said she went out but two or three times a year. Who knows what she did after I left? Made columns of numbers and added them up, I suppose, or walked around checking her dials. Maybe she

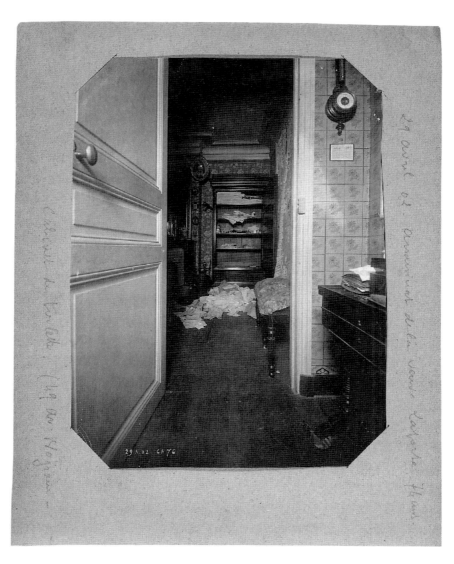

29 APRIL 1902, MURDER OF WIDOW LAPORTE, AGE 74

Cabinet de toilette (49 Av. Wagram)

DISCOVERY OF THE BODY

spread out her money, to look at or count. That's what I'd have done. I'd want to see it piled up, glowing under the lamp.

Close to the time she was killed, her lawyer came by. I brought coffee to the sitting room while they talked about adding another building to her properties. She was selling some of her titles. "Dear monsieur, *liquide*! I always pay cash," she told him. For this purchase maybe more got added to the money in her apartment. Her kids stood to inherit, but she was not on speaking terms with her daughter, which is why she lived alone. None of them ever showed up while I was there.

I learned for myself about her being murdered. When I got to the apartment, it was roped off. A policeman, standing guard, told me to turn around and go home. "You don't have a job anymore." He thought he was being funny. I didn't.

The building was in uproar, her neighbors all jitters, peeking out their doors, trying to catch something they could talk about. Their eyes were glued on the detectives who were stomping around, yelling orders and dropping ash on the carpets. A bad smell came from flashing explosions: a photographer making pictures of the scene.

They said the killer tied her with a pillow case he tore in pieces and her face was black and twisted. Monsieur Cochefert, the chief detective, asked how long I worked for Madame Laporte, and what she was like. I don't snitch on my ladies, especially when they've passed on and can't defend themselves. So I acted ignorant. I was mute about her money. That he'd have to find out by himself.

"Whoever snuffed her came in after I left, when she was alone," said I. "Last I saw she was wearing a white shift, her black peignoir, and a black wool fichu. She had on violet stockings and cloth slippers."

I prided myself on noticing. The newspapers always say what the person wore. Anyhow, it's what the widow always wore. That's exactly how she looked, he told me, adding her face was calm and dignified.

Neighbors said a pillow case was stuffed in her mouth, and her neck had blue marks from a heavy security chain the killer pulled off the door to her apartment. They said a crowbar was next to the body. I'm used to miseries I read in the papers, but some things make you sick. I'm thinking the chain meant a bully broke in and got her. I didn't do the detective's job by saying anything.

I asked Monsieur Cochefert whether I should clean up. The place was a wreck. Only the widow knew who did that. The police acting like it was theirs made it worse. She'd have hated linens pulled from her armoire, spread all over the floor. "Go home. We won't need your help. You'll ruin the evidence."

The robber knew her furniture was filled with money. How? I'd seen it, that was our secret, me and the widow's. He took all the cash she had on hand. Maybe the other maids before me knew about it too. I thought about this and realized the widow owed me a week's wages. She was even holding some of my money for safekeeping. "It'll teach you to save," she'd said. How can I get what's coming to me now? She's gone. I've no proof my money was mixed with hers.

I stood thinking how *I*'d been robbed. I wanted to cry. Dying all of a sudden, the widow really let me down. Police were scurrying about, pulling out drawers to see what was missing. They found 700 francs in a pile of sheets. Maybe they took certain things for themselves, souvenirs for their wives and sweethearts. I said to myself, better get in there and snatch something to sell. You earned it.

I told a policeman I had left a few personal things in the kitchen. He let me pass though the seals. I was alone in the scullery. I reached in a cabinet and took some flowered faience. I'd had my eye on those plates. They were chipped, not bad though. The good ones were on the walls in the dining room. I didn't mind second-best. I wrapped them in a towel and put them it in my satchel.

I walked like a cat to get past the chief detective. Didn't want nothing clattering. He seemed more nervous than me with a lot on his mind.

"This is the third rich old lady in two months who's been robbed and killed," he was telling an agent.

The detective's going to find all the maids who worked for Widow Laporte and ask them questions like he did me. Turns out she'd had forty in three years. After money, they said, all she thought about were her maids. I can testify to that, but I'm wondering how's he going to find the rest of them. I figure one probably set her boyfriend to it. Using a crowbar and a chain on the widow, he had to be a professional.

I loved her money too. That's why she didn't fire me so fast. I felt like we were sisters with her secret. We never talked about it or anything else that mattered. Like thieves, we ate our lunch without a word. I won't sell her plates. I'll keep them to remember her by.

I went to Notre-Dame to the funeral. To pay my respects. I also wanted to study the crowd. Maybe one of the other maids would be there wearing a strange expression. I'd point her out to the police and collect the money they pay informers.

It's bad luck to criticize the dead, but the funeral was a sorry affair. They put my employer in a pine box and threw it on a shabby hearse. Widow Laporte was rich, but she left this world a pauper, buried at the state's expense. Her children can't be blamed. They were waiting for their birthright. With this stolen, they didn't have enough of their own to give her a proper farewell. So they claimed. My kids won't treat me like that. I'm saving for a decent burial.

Only a dozen people were in the procession to the cemetery. I'm not surprised. She didn't know anyone, except maids and lawyers. I gave them a look-over as they passed along the curbs. Nobody stuck out. I joined the parade, keeping my eye on the coffin, imagining my lady inside, asleep on her money. I fancied a few coins, escaping the detectives and the doctor at the morgue, lighting the way to her reward.

The plates I took hardly compare with the money I saw in her bed. It wasn't my fancy. The money was real! Whoever killed her is out there in a new suit of clothes, pissing away her stash. Because of him I lost my job and what she was keeping for me. Without her signature for a reference I'm doomed to public assistance.

Her son and daughter won't do much better. What a miserable pair, leading the mourners. Thought they'd be rich. They weren't counting on someone getting to their *maman*'s treasure before they did. I got my plates. All they'll get is a bunch of barometers!

THE CRIME ON THE AVENUE DE WAGRAM

On 3 May Monsieur Cochefert went to the town of Houillés and lengthily questioned Monsieur D., who for thirty-five years was a friend and confidant of Madame Laporte. While this gentleman was unable to throw light on a possible assassin, he added that Madame Laporte spent no more than 3,000 francs of her yearly income. She saved the rest, which amounted to at least 20,000 francs a year. He also mentioned that she did not keep this money in her possession but placed it with two notaries in the provinces whose names and addresses he furnished. The theft would not seem to have been as important as one had believed.

Le Figaro, 4 May 1902

24 Trivial Things That Catch the Light

30 April 1902, 17 Rue Croix-des-Vignes,
Gennevilliers, northwest of Paris,
Joseph Escudé, 19, clerk in the creamery
of Widow Renaud, robbed and suffocated
by five young men from Saint-Denis.
Tissier, Durand, and Lépineux were
condemned to forced labor for life, Chabanne
was sentenced to five years of solitary
confinement for conceiving the crime while
Lelièvre was acquitted.

The sky over Gennevilliers is grey, but everything's in bud, and Madame Renaud's caged canaries are warbling in the courtyard of her creamery. The place looks deserted. This morning the old lady left for the Clichy market to sell her eggs, cheese, and butter. She took along her daughter and son-in-law, Monsieur Vatan, plus a maid and a clerk, leaving Joseph Escudé, another clerk, to watch the place and pay the bank messengers from 5,000 francs she left on the dining room table.

It is past noon. In the shadows of Madame Renaud's stable, Joseph lies dying. He has lost his clogs. A rag has been stuffed down his throat. A scarf is double-knotted around his neck. An apron, also tied around his neck, covers his head. His arms are bound to his sides, and his legs are bundled with a leather girth. He looks like a bale of hay. Tears on his face have attracted a colony of flies. These and the singing birds remind him he's still alive.

His rage also reminds him. Scarcely able to draw a breath, he feels his heart slow to that of a tortoise. For weeks he's been anxious. A group of five young men has been scouting the Rue Croix-des-Vignes, studying the creamery and the movements of the customers. They gestured and mouthed whispers, calculating when he'd be alone. Now he knows why. They waited for market day because then the bank messengers come for payments, and a large sum of money is in the house.

Today three of these skulkers burst through the iron grill and knocked Joseph down. He tore their cheeks with his fingernails, punched them with his fists. He's tall and strong, but he wishes he'd been bolder. He should have speared them with a pitchfork before they trussed him. Gulping air past the rag in his throat, he hears them ransack the house. They dance when they see the money and laugh as they drag Madame Renaud's safe from the bedroom down the narrow staircase. They stand right beside him when they hitch the horse to a cart and load the safe, and then they leave.

He thinks they probably looked silly weighing down the tiny vehicle. They won't get far in their clumsy escape. Everyone on the street knows Madame Renaud's red cart. Her beautiful chestnut mare is famous. Neighbors will notice the safe. Someone will run to the stable and find him before he dies. He will testify against these fiends in criminal court. Until then, he must stay alive . . .

* * *

Cochefert has taken the number 39 tram from the Madeleine to Gennevilliers to investigate the murder of a boy in a creamery. Crammed into the seat, the huge detective winces, envisioning the formula of small-town misery: the boy laid out in the stable next to baskets of eggs and cheese, the collapsing mother, stupefied comrades, incredulous employers, officials, fat and breathless, leading the funeral cortège and carrying outsized wreathes dedicated to the deceased. Everyone railing, "Scoundrels! Villains!" against the uncaught killers like a chorus on cue. Add to this details the press loves: thieves who work the crowd and steal the mourners' purses.

Cochefert likes such ironies, the misery of ignorant folk, the hidden wickedness of the countryside. He watches the Seine move northward in a hairpin loop around the Gennevilliers plain toward Argenteuil thinking of how important it is right now to penetrate the cruelty of depraved villagers. He wants to hunt them in the open air, track them along footpaths, under bridges, and into poplar groves like a bloodhound needs the scent.

As the tram crosses the Seine through the Ile des Ravageurs, Cochefert strains to see the Dog Cemetery. He used to spend afternoons in this city of dead canines, copying famous epithets into his notebook: "We loved her too much. She could not live." Or Pascal's, "Man is only a thinking animal," or Chamfort's "The more I see of men, the more I love my dog." Cochefert isn't so cynical. He loves his work and the tortured minds of criminals even more. Still, the pious phrases engraved on the stones have the power to move him to tears.

He strains to see the tomb of Loulou who died saving a child from drowning, or that of brave Bijou who rescued his mistress from a criminal attack, or the stone of Caporal "who died at age eleven leaving 150 descendants," or the grave of Gazouillis "a little blind finch loved by three children."

His favorite tomb, at the entrance, has a white marble statue of Barry, a beautiful Saint Bernard who "saved the lives of forty men and was killed by the forty-first." His skin is preserved in the Natural History Museum in Berne. Cochefert loves sad-eyed Barry, a big dog like himself whose last case destroyed him. He speculates that the murder in the creamery won't bring him down—gangs of boys are easy to convict, especially dumb ones from the country. Yet the press is regularly publishing lists of his unsolved crimes and Cochefert has a feeling that his career won't last much longer. Gennevilliers is close. A foul stench invades the car from the factories at Asnières and from the Paris sewage pouring into the Seine which floods the Gennevilliers plain. The farmers don't notice the odor of this fertilizer any more because everything grows so well. Maybe the infection lives silently in the vegetables, he thinks, and gives the children brain fever so they grow up to be murderers.

Through the window Cochefert sees somber potato fields. Meandering brooks become silver threads in the grey light, reminding him of the painters, twenty-five years ago, who glorified these places with every color of the spectrum. They claimed to be supreme observers. By his standards they were narcissists who escaped their studios to paint thin air.

He saw them bribe café owners to sit on the terrace and paint the crowds. They liked trivial things that caught the light: a hat trimmed with artificial cherries; yellow gloves holding a glass of chartreuse. He remembered them in railroad stations. Let them take his place with Bertillon's picture of a criminal's ear, trying to nab the poor bastard picking pockets, Cochefert thought, or tell them to use it to nail a pickpocket at the Saint-Lazare railroad station, and we'd see what kind of observers they were.

Cochefert remembered these painters flocking to the suburbs. The places they'd come to paint were open conduits of black filth, the same filth stinking up his tram. The wicked atmosphere never tainted the pictures. Painting impressions meant keeping a safe distance from the odors of decay. It favored the charms of parasols, bustles, sails, and light between the trees. It ignored death, darkness, motive, everything fully human, for a world of eternal noons.

Cochefert prides himself in seeing through flickering surfaces. Details to him are matters of life and death which prove evil intent and solve crimes.

* * *

AFFAIR OF GENNEVILLIERS, MURDER OF MONSIEUR ESCUDÉ, I. 5. 1902

House of the crime

Cour interieur : maison de M. V. Renaud

INTERIOR COURT, HOUSE OF M.V. RENAUD

As Cochefert heads toward Gennevilliers, a sanctuary of impression-istic sensation, he makes himself dizzy with thoughts about artists. They'd see young people drinking in a wine shop at Villeneuve-la-Garenne and improve the tired faces with cadmium reflections from a striped awning overhead. They'd hear these drinkers complaining about a bankrupt butter business and imprisonment for selling without a license, but they wouldn't capture the bruised glances or nervous shaking of hands and heads. A police agent, pretending to study a newspaper at the next table, would strain to hear boys begging an older companion to tell them of a job they could pull to rob a butter seller of his extra "fat."

A group of four young men might leave a wine shop on the Argenteuil quay. They might shock the proprietor by paying with a five-franc gold piece, engraved with the head of Ferdinand VII of the Kingdom of the Two Sicilies, vintage 1856, and out of circulation for years. Cochefert, pretending to buy spinach, would overhear one young man tell a greengrocer in Saint-Denis that he'd put some friends up to robbing a creamery, that they suffocated the clerk and left him to die in a stable. He would have made a clear mental des-cription of the young man begging the grocer for an alibi by bribing his wife with a stolen watch.

Walking through Gennevilliers the chief detective doesn't see anyone painting. Manet and Caillebotte are dead; Madame Morisot, the citizens' favorite, who gave costume balls in Gennevilliers and glorified mothers and children in the sunshine of her husband's pro-perty, has fled the putrefaction for Bougival. Monet is secluded in Giverny, fighting off the rats that devour his water-lily bulbs.

Cochefert's form throws a grotesque shadow as he strolls the town looking for clues. On the Rue Croix-des-Vignes he finds Hyvert, a boy Joseph's age who bought eggs an hour before the crime. Hyvert had noticed some young men sitting in Madame Renaud's English cart, hitched to a chestnut horse outside her iron gate. He'd seen another close the gate, mount the cart, and make a strange military salute toward the stable, wiggling his fingers in a sneering "bye-bye." It hadn't occurred to Hyvert to investigate what was behind it.

Other neighbors describe the cart to the detective from Paris. Of course, they say, it had looked odd, listing dangerously. The passengers hardly fled. They couldn't whip the horse beyond a walk. The vehicle cruised like a festival float in the spring haze, fairly welcoming the attention of bystanders. When Monsieur Manceau asked what was wrong with the cart, why it seemed so heavy, he said their faces froze. "Their surly mouths were like clocks, reading eight-twenty." One stood up and curdled Manceau with a obscenity. He was so stunned he didn't identify the conveyance as Madame Renaud's. He didn't associate the horse with her stable. He didn't think to close the iron grill of her courtyard which had swung open, or enter the shadows where Joseph lay choking. "I asked the fellow a simple question, and he grossly insulted me in front of my neighbors."

Cochefert has a local policeman drive him to a field near the Seine called "The Burnt Poplar." Yesterday, at four, light around the tree would have blazed golden rays on the party of young men arriving in an English cart. It would have glanced off their caps and caught the ruddy coat of the mare as they freed it from its harness. It would have struck the buttons of one who left and returned with another accomplice. It would have engulfed them in gorgeous red madder as they dragged the safe from the cart.

Cochefert squints to grasp the effect. From his position, the party would have seemed to be picnicking with a hamper of food and wine. But after attacking the box with chisels, crowbars and hammers, these revelers weren't handing around sliced paté. They were dividing 5,000 francs from Madame Renaud's dining room table and 7,500 francs from her strong-box. Raising their arms in a toast, they were actually trying on the jewels, rolling on damp grass, laughing, half drunk, as sun scorched the clouds. After two left in the direction of Epinay, the others dragged the box to the river and watched it sink.

MURDER OF GENNEVILLIERS

Affair of Gennevilliers, Murder of Monsieur Escudé, 1. 5. 1902
Discovery of the body of Joseph Escudé

Cochefert might have been the shepherd grazing his flock a few meters away. Since the actual scene glowed like a painting, the young murderers wouldn't have noticed the keeper of the herd as a possible witness. He was a picturesque detail on the periphery. Later he positively identified every one of them.

Cochefert returns to Gennevilliers. His agents recover the safe. He collects the killers, one by one. They make his job easy. They can't stop talking. A greengrocer in Saint-Denis sends him after Louis Chabanne, a bankrupt butter seller who dreamed up the crime, panicked, confessed the whole thing to him, then tried to wangle an alibi by giving his wife a gold watch. No stealth in these bumpkins. Cochefert laughs. He forces Chabanne to name his accomplices. There's Lelièvre, called "Lapin," rabbit, Félix Tissier, and Durand, called "Grosse Tête," fat head. The latter two he finds in Murat at the Hotel Boum-Boum, celebrating with wine after having made a down payment toward a banquet for thirty members of Tissier's family in honor of Durand's engagement to his sister. Cochefert finds bloody fingernail cuts on their hands and faces. As he brings them in chains to the police carriage, a crowd outside the hotel tries to stone them. "We weren't supposed to kill the clerk. The plan was to tie him up and rob the house!"

It takes a month to find "Nénesse," Ernest Lépineux, the really dangerous member of the gang whom the others insist actually killed the clerk. Lépineux has trouble controlling himself. He enjoys beating people up. He gets excited when they resist. Cochefert discovers he's a deserter, an escapee from military prison having been sentenced by the war council of the 132nd infantry unit at Reims for trying to strangle one of his superiors.

Meanness wasn't enough for them to succeed, Cochefert thinks. They weren't artists enough to be criminals. They weren't capable of art's necessary silence and vagary. The oafish boys of the Gennevilliers plain spilled everything. Their failed scheme struck the detective as boring. Sad as a factory.

25 Digits

16 October 1902, 157 Rue du Faubourg
Saint-Honoré, VIIIth Arrondissement,
Joseph Reibel, 45, valet, strangled in the office
of his employer, Dr Auguste Alaux, dental
surgeon, by Henri-Léon Scheffer, 26, thief,
prostitute. Sentenced to forced labor for life.

On 17 October 1902 I was ordered to take photographs at an office where the valet of Dr Alaux, a fashionable dental surgeon, had been murdered. Nothing unusual in the request. During my career as Chief of Judicial Identity I'd responded to hundreds of them. The place consisted of six rooms, lavishly furnished—one even had a grand piano—with salons for waiting patients and operating rooms. The dentist lived elsewhere. Leaving work each day at five, he had his valet, Joseph Reibel, watch the premises. As I said, they were filled with treasures.

Next morning when the dentist rang, Reibel didn't answer. So he opened the door with his own key and found Reibel lying on his back, supported by an overturned chair. His face carried fingernail scratches. A napkin was knotted around his neck, and his dental plate was shoved down his throat. On a table were two glasses and a bottle of rum. Reibel obviously was drinking with someone who'd strangled him, between five and six the previous evening, and smashed the furniture in search of valuables.

Investigations become idiotic when you don't know how to look. My colleague, the ingenious, magical Armand Cochefert, Chief of Criminal Investigation, began searching for the murderer among the victim's friends, based on Alaux's assertion that his servant, an "inveterate homosexual," brought home many individuals of "strange aspect." One, Alfred Plomb, came to collect a forgotten umbrella before the time of the crime but could prove he was at a music hall all evening. Cochefert suspected him because Plomb claimed that the dentist, fed up with Reibel's eternal tippling—drinking the dregs of his wine bottles, stealing his cigars—promised to give him, Plomb, the valet's job on the condition that he cut his mustache. Hardly a reason to strangle someone with your bare hands!

Cochefert then thought he had an important witness: Monsieur Cayla, a wine merchant, said Reibel entered his shop at five-twenty, downed a glass, and announced he was going to be alone that evening. Was he overheard? Reibel left at five-fifty, Cayla said. It was pouring rain. No one accompanied him. But what does that prove?

Cochefert found several letters to Reibel he thought "might interest justice." We never learned what they contained. Reibel's brother testified that the victim was receiving interest on 4,000 francs, which he'd recently given to an insurance company to convert into a life annuity. Motive for murder? By whom?

Out of ideas, Cochefert ordered the privy hole of Alaux's building emptied, hoping to find the stolen objects. Wallowing in excrement, his agents retrieved nothing. "Truth is not always in a well," Poe's marvelous detective C. Auguste Dupin says. Then Cochefert found a vegetable seller who said he saw Reibel talking with someone outside Cayla's wine shop—this had to be the murderer. But the poor fellow was legally blind. What can he have seen? Cochefert, ever the trickster, was playing at criminology. "The ingenious are always fanciful," Dupin says. But "the *truly* imaginative" are "never otherwise than analytic." Which is where I came in. In a week I positively identified the killer.

AFFAIR ALAUX, FAUBOURG SAINT-HONORÉ

AFFAIR ALAUX, FAUBOURG SAINT-HONORÉ

AFFAIR ALAUX, FAUBOURG SAINT-HONORÉ

Photographing crime scenes depresses me. Disorder. Stench. Blood. Twisted faces. The dentist's rooms were very dark, needing long exposures which in the images made the furniture and objects seem to palpitate with their own psychic life. Had I believed Commander Darget's theory of magnetic effluvia, I'd have thought the papers, statues, mirrors, chandeliers — torpid witnesses to the crime — were exerting their own wills, emanating a sulfurous "light of truth" which, properly interpreted, might reveal the murderer whose body heat had left its aura everywhere.

Engrossed, like Dupin, in these "deviations from the plane of the ordinary," I was gradually drawn to the broken pane of a glass showcase against the wall next to a painted portrait in the piano room. Someone had tried to remove the glass in order to snatch the valuables inside, but failing this, left clearly visible fingerprints. I carried the piece of glass to my laboratory and with great difficulty succeeded in photographing the fingerprints on both sides of the transparency.

Since 1893, I'd been interested in the absolutely identifying powers claimed for marks made by the hand — on glass, polished furniture, marble, etc. — and began adding fingerprints to my anthropometric cards. But I'd never put them to the test. It didn't take long for my archivists to exactly match the prints I photographed at the dentist's to a set of prints on file. They belonged to Henri-Léon Scheffer, the victim's lover.

From the address of Scheffer's mother on my card, the police intercepted a letter he wrote after the crime asking her for money, giving the name of Georges Boulery and a Marseilles address. Cochefert had Scheffer detained in that city where the suspect awaited the money to sail to Argentina, having lost all he'd stolen from Alaux at the races, and claiming later to have tossed the plundered jewels into the sea. In Paris, Scheffer confessed, saying he and Reibel collaborated to rob the dentist by simulating a break-in, but during an argument over the spoils he strangled his partner.

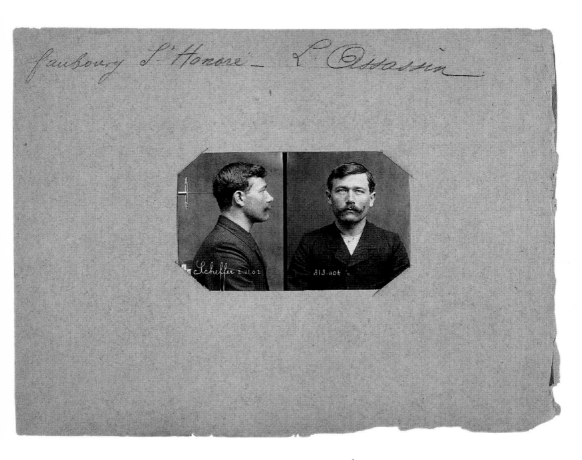

AFFAIR ALAUX, FAUBOURG SAINT-HONORÉ: THE MURDERER

Scheffer, 2. 11. 02

At Scheffer's trial I showed the jury the fingerprint photographs, enlarged ten times, so they could see the nearly concentric grooves in each of the fingers. Then I established more than 100 characteristic signs of the same pattern on the prints we'd made when Scheffer was previously detained. Everyone found my process "extremely curious," but convincing.

"Did you leave these prints?" the judge asked the accused.

"Oui, Monsieur."

The press called the crime the first in France, perhaps in Europe, solved exclusively through fingerprints.

* * *

"Truth is invariably superficial," Dupin says, and I agree. But I prefer to think of Scheffer, confronting his tell-tale tracery, as Pascal put it, "terrified at himself."

It would be presumptuous of me to assume that I even approach Pascal's knowledge, much less his spiritual humility and deep human compassion. Yet my science has been my sole reason for living. Many find the techniques too exacting. But no one will deny that they established the standard of modern police surveillance. I'm proud to say that because of my efforts, we can gather the entire world under one roof, as the Universal Exhibition strove to do with such grandeur. My anthropometric cabinets, towers rising to infinity, capable of unraveling mankind, endlessly proclaim God's magnificent design. Compared to the nothingness beyond our reach, the body of the lowest criminal is a colossus, a world. His form, marvelously intricate, always recognizable, links him with the infinite, from his ear's tiny landscape, to the shallowest furrows on his thumb.

Armand Cochefert (*16 March 1850) had to resign as Chief of Criminal Investigation in November 1902, not because of the growing number of unsolved murder cases but due to his apparent negligence in the Humbert-Crawford affair, a large-scale fraud case involving an impostor and a son of a former Minister of Justice. He died in Auteuil on 5 September 1911.

Alphonse Bertillon (*22 April 1853) died from pernicious anemia on 13 February 1914. Sixty-one and blind, he was asked on his deathbed to retract his opinion regarding Dreyfus, by then legally declared innocent. He refused.

ARMAND COCHEFERT

ALPHONSE BERTILLON

Dedication

"Murderers are easy to understand."

Rainer Maria Rilke

He was the eldest: his mother's only son; a prince among impoverished Greek peasants. America is your great opportunity, they said. But he knew he was the family sacrifice, the best they had to give away.

In 1911 his father led him from his village games, and they sailed to America. The father returned to the Peloponnesus, leaving him to work as a busboy in an uncle's café on Halsted Street in Chicago and send back money so his four sisters would have dowries.

He was ten, too young for men's work, too intelligent to spend sixteen hours a day scraping dirty dishes. It shows in a photograph made soon after he arrived. Probably it was the first time he'd seen a camera. Seated on a bentwood chair in a yard behind the café, he tries to look confident. One hand takes root on a table top; the other spreads over his thigh. The new city boy in cap, knickers, suspenders, and dark stockings feigns dignity, but his feet hardly touch the ground.

Through a window, a kitchen helper, another Greek, studies this imperious nephew getting special treatment. The intruder doesn't see the boy's clouded detachment. He doesn't know he's watching a child who, torn from his mother, deprived of the terraced fields, familiar stones and roads, the pines and golden light of his native Arcadia, feels he's been murdered.

In a year he left the café, lived at the YMCA, and worked delivering telegrams on a bicycle. He lost his true love in the influenza epidemic of 1918. He became American, changing Demetrios Petro-poulos to Daniel Parry in order to practice law in a town he perceived as dominated by the Irish. Later, he named himself Demetri Parry. His was the story of thousands of successful immigrants.

Another story says the sacrifice was too great. He despaired and grew rageful, plotted revenge on imagined foes, wrote furious letters exposing anyone who seemed odd to him. At age seventy he put five bullets into another Greek immigrant, a crony from the YMCA days. For this he target-practiced for twenty years, deep in a Michigan wood, so when the voices urged him, he was ready. This is how I knew him: quick to violence, preoccupied, consumed by secrets and mysterious apparitions. I didn't know what these things meant.

The photograph of him at ten shows the murderer before com-mitting his crime, the village-child-voyager, an important part of whom is dormant, perhaps already dead. He was my father. This book is dedicated to him as he was then.

Eugenia Parry

DEMETRIOS PETROPOULOS (1901–1981)

Acknowledgments

I am indebted to many friends and associates and warmly thank them all. For particular contributions, I am grateful to the following in

PARIS

Gérard Lévy, owner of the album, who in 1971 with his former partner, François Lepage, first showed me this strange object. André Le Cudennec, Secrétaire administratif des Archives historiques de la Préfecture de Police, guided me through memoirs, *dossiers* and morgue ledgers; Sylvain Pelly carefully photographed the album for this publication; Sylvie Aubenas, Bibliothèque Nationale de France, and collector Serge Kakou, inspired me with their passion for pictures. André Jammes lent me texts by Bertillon. The late Harry Lunn Jr. tirelessly obtained maps and important photographs of Bertillon's method and with Myriam Lunn extended infinite kindness and hospitality.

NEW YORK

Maria Morris Hambourg, Metropolitan Museum of Art; John Szarkowski; Pierre Apraxine; Jill Quasha; Jim Mairs of W. W. Norton and Co.

NEW MEXICO

Fred Chris Smith, former State Prosecutor and Director of Prosecution for the State of New Mexico, showed me what crime-scene photographs actually mean in crime solving. Tom Barrow, University of New Mexico; John Talley, M.D.; Jack Woody, Twin Palms Publishers. James Crump of Arena Editions, Jenifer Blakemore, Dennis Jarrett, and Miriam Sagan read many stories at various stages.

Librarians Brian Freels and Randy Moorehead at the University of New Mexico, Albuquerque; the staff of the New Mexico State Library, Santa Fe, and of Saint John's College, Santa Fe, obtained crucial documents.

MASSACHUSETTS

George Shackelford, Museum of Fine Arts, Boston; Anne McCauley, University of Massachusetts, Boston; Michael Wentworth, The Boston Athenaeum; Robert Pinsky; Rosamund Purcell; the staff and resources of the Harvard University Science Libraries, Cambridge. Elsa Dorfman read many stories early on, W. S. MacNeil read them repeatedly for years.

LOUISIANA

Benjamin F. Martin, Professor of History, Louisiana State University, Baton Rouge, gave sound advice at the outset.

ZURICH, BERLIN, NEW YORK

Walter Keller of Scalo instantly grasped what I was trying to do; Martin Jäggi and Theres Abbt shared inspired, if brief conversations. Hans Werner Holzwarth designed this book beautifully. My editor, the incomparable Alexis Schwarzenbach, selected twenty-five stories from the forty I wrote and gave me the courage to love their bones laid bare.

* * *

A grant in literature (creative non-fiction) from the National Endowment for the Arts (1993) was decisive in allowing me to leave university teaching and devote myself to writing full-time.

Writer Brent Jarrett, exercised a daily influence. Through his sage humor and uncanny critical perception, my writing became stories.